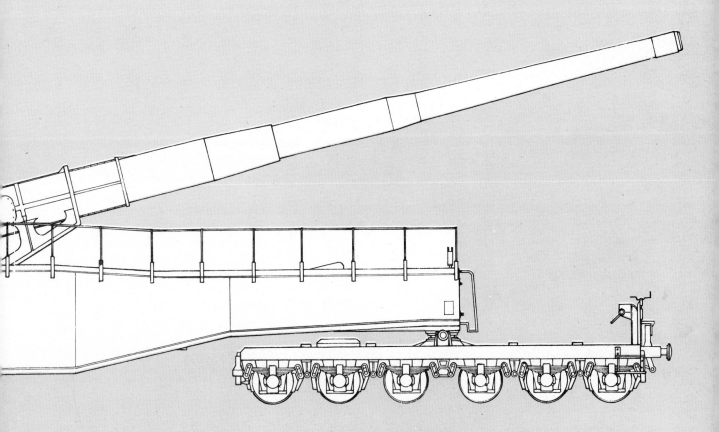

The Illustrated Encyclopedia of 20th Century

WEAPONS AND WARFARE

The Illustrated Encyclopedia of 20th Century

WEAPONS AND WARFARE

COLUMBIA HOUSE/New York

Editor: Bernard Fitzsimons
Designer: David Harper
Editorial Assistants: Suzanne Pearce
                      Robin Cross
                      Sarie Forster
                      Will Fowler
Production: Tony Holdsworth
Picture Research: Diane Rich
Editorial Director: Graham Donaldson

BERNARD FITZSIMONS, General Editor
ANTONY PRESTON, Naval Consultant
BILL GUNSTON, Aviation Consultant
IAN V. HOGG, Land Weapons Consultant

JOHN BATCHELOR, Illustrator

Cover Design: Harry W. Fass
Production Manager: Stephen Charkow

"We shall not flag or fail. We shall fight in France, we shall fight on the seas and oceans, we shall fight with growing confidence and growing strength in the air, we shall defend our island, whatever the cost may be, we shall fight on the beaches, we shall fight on the landing grounds, we shall fight in the fields and in the streets, we shall fight in the hills; we shall never surrender."

—Winston Churchill on Dunkirk.
Speech to the House of Commons
June 4, 1940

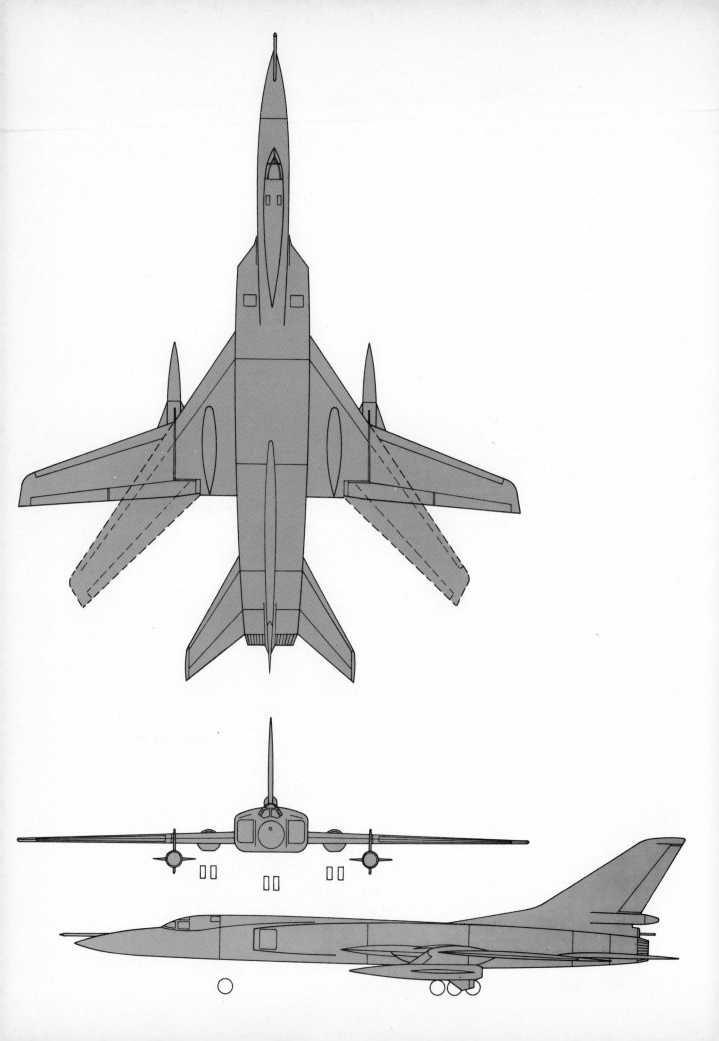

INTRODUCTION

The weapons covered in Volume 3 again form an extremely varied collection. Every type of weapon is represented and virtually the entire range of 20th-Century development is covered.

Submarines, for example, often dismissed as rather uninteresting "gray metal cigars," were a new addition to most navies at the start of the century and, for the most part, were regarded as useless novelties. Although Sergeant Ezra Lee, in David Bushnell's *Turtle*, had come within an ace of sinking the British flagship in the Hudson River in 1776, it was not until the First World War that the submarine came to be a useful weapon of war.

In this Volume we show, in color cutaway and line detail, two representatives of the first stage of modern submarine development. The British and Norwegian *"B" Classes* were both based on the ideas of John P. Holland, one of the great pioneers of submarines. As well as a color cutaway of the British boat, an interesting sidelight is a drawing—taken from the official plans—of one of the vessels converted to a surface patrol boat. And it is fascinating to note that although the Norwegian vessels built in the early 1920s were virtually the final stage in the evolution of Holland's ideas, they embodied many of the features to be found in the most modern submarines—of which the *Barbel* and the *Benjamin J. Franklin* (also included here) —are typical examples.

And, as an example of the "half-way" stage in development, the *Balao Class*—one of the largest classes of submarines ever built—is here too. As well as having a fine war record in the Pacific, the *Balao Class* provided the first submarines ever equipped to launch guided missiles. In 1947-48, the *Carbonero* and *Cusk*, were fitted with hangars and launching ramps for the *Republic JB-2 Loon* copy of the *German V-1*. Tests were completed successfully, as shown in our photographs, and formed the first step in the progression toward the *Posei-*

don submarines of the 1970s.

Another weapon unique to the 20th Century is the *Bomber*. When war broke out in France in 1914, aircraft were barely capable of lifting bombs, let alone providing a useful offensive capability. Yet today, *strategic bombers*, along with *nuclear submarines* and *land-based ICBMs*, are part of the front line of national defense. In the pages of this Volume a selection of aircraft illustrate the full range of bomber development.

The *British B.E. Series* of the First World War were some of the earliest bomber types, while the *Curtis B2*, *Douglas B-7* and *B-18*, and the *Boeing B-9*, along with the *Japanese Navy bombers*, demonstrate the progress made between the World Wars.

The *Convair B-36*, designed to bomb German-occupied Europe from bases in the United States, was the first truly intercontinental bomber; the *Ilyushin 11-28 Beagle* was the first Soviet jet bomber; and the story is completed by the *Rockwell B-1*—illustrated by superbly detailed plans—and the *Tupolev Backfire*, the latest U.S. and Soviet bombers.

As well as describing the technical aspects of these aircraft, the author offers an informed assessment of the role of the *manned bomber* in general, and the *B-1* and the *Backfire* in particular, in future national defense.

The *Artillery Section*, too, covers a broad range of hardware. *German heavy flak, heavy antitank*, and *medium field guns* are described and illustrated, along with perhaps the most awesome artillery types—the mighty *Rail Guns*. These huge guns were so complex and their stories are so interesting that most will be discussed under their own names. The survey included here, however, covers all the main types of *German Rail Gun*, including the phenomenal *Paris Gun*, built to bombard Paris in 1917 with the incredible range of 70 miles.

Avro 504

British multirole biplane. Though a simple low-powered machine flown before the start of the First World War, the Avro 504 was made in larger numbers than any other aircraft prior to the Second World War, and served in many air forces for more than 20 years. The first numbered Avro design, Mr A V Roe's Type 500, was ordered by the RFC in early 1913 as the Type E. Very similar, and likewise powered by the 80-hp Gnome rotary engine, the 504 flew in July 1913, and in November set a measured speed of 130.2 km/h (80.9 mph), and soon afterwards a British altitude record at 4395 m (14 420 ft).

A total of 63 early models were supplied to the RFC (one was shot down on scouting duty over the Western Front as early as August 22, 1914) and RNAS. The RNAS used their machines as strategic bombers, three flying as single-seaters from Belfort on November 21, 1914, each carrying four 9-kg (20-lb) bombs dropped on the Zeppelin assembly sheds and hangars (and a gasworks) at Friedrichshafen. Such raids became impossible with the advance of German ground forces, but the RNAS machines continued to fight the enemy in every way, with light bombs under the wings and an observer in the front cockpit manning a 7.7-mm Lewis gun. Two U-Boats were destroyed in a raid

by RNAS 504s on the submarine base at Antwerp, while many missions were flown in the ground-strafing role.

Bulk production began with the RFC 504A (shorter ailerons) and RNAS 504B (normal ailerons but a fixed fin). Single-seat fighter conversions included 80 RNAS 504C with front cockpit faired over and, typically, a pilot-aimed Lewis on the upper centre section. A few carried Le Prieur rockets or Ranken incendiary darts for anti-Zeppelin missions. The RFC counterpart was the 504D but this was not built in quantity.

There were many other sub-types, but the next major development was the 504J of 1916, in which the Gnome was replaced by the 100-hp Gnome Monosoupape. This was the first purpose-designed military trainer and was the aircraft which laid the foundation for all subsequent flying training in all countries. It was similar to the refined 504K, which was designed to be powered by any of the available engines such as the 100-hp Mono, 110-hp Le Rhône or 130-hp Clerget. In early 1918 the more powerful K sub-types were again hurriedly converted into single-seat anti-Zeppelin fighters, equipping six Home Defence squadrons. The final wartime production version was the 504L float-seaplane. Total wartime production of the 504 in Britain amounted to 8340.

After 1918 new versions continued to

Avro 504A. This first sub-type of the basic machine retained the 80-hp Gnome engine but had ailerons of reduced span and interplane struts of broader chord. The 504A was built in considerable numbers by several manufacturers

appear, the most important being the 504N or Lynx Avro, with a more modern appearance without a skid between the mainwheels and with an Armstrong Siddeley Lynx radial of 160, 180 or 215 hp. Two fuel tanks were fitted under the upper wing and the fuselage was no longer square-sectioned. This continued in production as an RAF primary trainer until 1933, which brought total production in Britain to considerably over 10 000 A very small additional number were built in Canada in 1918, and a much larger number, probably exceeding 1000, were built in the Soviet Union with the designation U-1 between 1925 and 1933. The 504 had been an important type in the Revolutionary war in Russia, and was adopted by the Soviet government around 1922 as a standard interim multirole aircraft. Other 504s served with more than 30 air forces in the 1920s, many being fitted with floats or skis.

Among the uses to which the 504 was put, the outstanding reliability of the aircraft and the large numbers available led the autogyro pioneer Juan de la Cierva to use 504K fuselages as the basis of several of his Autogiros

Squadron Leader A W Bigsworth and the Avro 504B from which he dropped 20-lb bombs on the Zeppelin *LZ 39*, damaging the airship

Avro 504

(Cierva registered the name with this spelling) in the early 1920s. Avro went on to develop their own autogyros, initially in conjunction with Cierva, their first examples being replicas of Cierva's C-6A. Among subsequent machines was the Avro Rota, used by the RAF as a stationary target for radar calibration.

(504K) *Span:* 10.97 m (36 ft 0 in) *Length:* 8.97 m (29 ft 5 in) *Gross weight:* 830 kg (1830 lb) *Maximum speed:* 169 km/h (105 mph)

Avro British aircraft See **Aldershot, Anson, Lancaster, Lincoln, Manchester, Shackleton, Vulcan**

Avro Canada Canadian aircraft   See **CF-100**

Avtroil Russian destroyer class   See *Azard*

AW.38 British (Armstong Whitworth) aircraft See **Whitley**

AW.41 British (Armstrong Whitworth) aircraft See **Albemarle**

AWACS USAF Airborne warning and control system aircraft See **E-3 Boeing**

B.1 US submarine class   See *Cuttlefish*

No 874, one of the three Avro 504s which took part in the raid on the Zeppelin sheds at Friedrichshafen on November 21, 1914. Fitted with improvized racks for four 20-lb high-explosive bombs each and piloted by RNAS officers, they succeeded in damaging a Zeppelin and destroying the gasworks

One of the Spanish rotorcraft pioneer Juan de la Cierva's early Autogiros, the C-6 of 1924, based on the fuselage of an Avro 504K. Ailerons were fitted on outriggers, power supplied by a 110-hp le Rhône rotary engine, and lift provided by a 10.97-m (36-ft) diameter rotor. In late 1925 the C-6 was demonstrated at RAE Farnborough

Azard

Russian destroyer class. In 1912 the Imperial Russian Navy ordered a large number of destroyers as part of its programme to make good the losses of the war against Japan. Using the successful *Novik* as the prototype, 36 of a slightly enlarged version were ordered for the Baltic Fleet, and a further 17 for the Black Sea Fleet.

The order was divided into groups according to builders:

The *Azard* group of eight units, built by the Saint Petersburg Metal Works, had Parsons turbines and Thornycroft boilers. All were begun between mid-1914 and July 1915.

Name	launched	completed
Azard	6/1916	10/1916
Desna	11/1915	8/1916
Grom	5/1915	1/1916
Pobieditel	11/1914	11/1915
Zabiyaka	11/1914	11/1915
Samson	6/1915	12/1916
Orfei	11/1915	4/1916
Letun	11/1915	7/1916

The *Grom* was sunk by gunfire from the German battleship *Kaiser* on October 14, 1917, southeast of Hilu Maa Island. The *Orfei* and *Letun* were both damaged, the former in the autumn of 1917 and the latter on November 7, 1916, and both were laid up. By 1922 they were beyond repair and had to be scrapped, the *Letun* in 1925 and her sister four years later. The five survivors were refitted by the Soviets and formed the Type V group or *Artem* Class already described. Their names were changed as follows:

Azard renamed *Zinoviev* 1922, renamed *Artem* 1937;
Desna renamed *Engels* 1921;
Pobieditel renamed *Volodarsky* 1921;
Zabiyaka renamed *Uritzky* 1921;
Samson renamed *Stalin* 1921.

Displacement: 1260 tons (normal) *Length:* 98 m (321 ft 6 in) oa *Beam:* 9.3 m (30 ft 6 in) *Draught:* 3.2 m (10 ft 6 in) *Machinery:* 2-shaft Parsons steam turbines, 32 000 shp=35 knots *Armament:* 4 4-in (102-mm) (4×1); 9 17.7-in (45-cm) torpedo tubes (3×3); 50 mines *Crew:* 160

The *Gavriil* Class were laid down between December 1913 and January 1915 at the Russo-Baltic Works, Reval. As their turbines and boilers had been ordered in Germany the outbreak of war meant that three could not be completed.

The *Vladimir* was renamed *Svoboda* on September 12, 1917 and the *Leitenant Lombard* became *Mecheslav* on June 27 the same year. On October 21, 1919, while operating on a minelaying mission against the British Interventionist forces, the *Gavriil, Konstantin, Svoboda* and *Azard* ran into a British minefield off the coast of Estonia. Only the

Azard escaped, and the three destroyers were sunk with all hands. The incomplete hulls were towed to Saint Petersburg (then Petrograd) in February 1918 in an attempt to save them from the advancing Germans, but they were never completed and had to be scrapped in 1923.

Name	launched	completed
Gavriil	1/1915	10/1916
Konstantin	6/1915	5/1917
Vladimir	8/1915	1917
Mikhail	1916	—
Leitenant Lombard	1917	—
Sokol	1917	—

Displacement: 1350 tons (normal) *Length:* 107 m (351 ft 0 in) oa *Beam:* 9.4 m (30 ft 9 in) *Draught:* 3.9 m (12 ft 9 in) *Machinery:* 2-shaft steam turbines, 32 700 shp=35 knots *Armament:* 5 4-in (102-mm) (5×1); 9 17.7-in (45-cm) torpedo tubes (3×3) *Crew:* 168

Between October 1913 and November 1914 the new Putilov Works at Saint Petersburg laid down a further eight destroyers. Of similar design, they had German turbines and French boilers and were designed by Vulcan of Stettin.

Name	launched	completed
Kapitan Izylmetiev	11/1914	7/1916
Kapitan Kingsbergen	8/1915	12/1917
Leitenant Ilin	11/1914	12/1916
Kapitan Kern	8/1915	—
Kapitan Belli	10/1915	—
Kapitan Kroun	8/1916	—
Kapitan Konon-Zotov	10/1915	—
Leitenant Dubasov	9/1916	—

As with the previous group the names were changed to suit revolutionary tastes:

Kapitan Izylmetiev renamed *Lenin* 1921;
Kapitan Kingsbergen renamed *Kapitan Miklukha Maklei* on June 27, 1915, renamed *Spartak* December 18, 1918;
Leitenant Ilin renamed *Garibaldi* 1920, renamed *Trotsky* 1921, renamed *Voikov* 1927;
Kapitan Kern renamed *Rykov* 1927, renamed *Zhdanov* 1937, renamed *Valerian Kuibishev* 1939;
Kapitan Belli renamed *Karl Liebknecht* 1928.

The *Spartak* was no luckier with her new name. On December 26, 1918 she was sent to

Central Naval Museum, Leningrad

The Russian destroyer *Gavriil*, name ship of the second group of the *Azard* Class

reconnoitre Reval, where the British Interventionist forces under Admiral Cowan had just arrived. Unfortunately the British destroyers had steamed up, and when the *Spartak*'s shells began to fall in the harbour they weighed anchor and gave chase.

Pausing only to send the signal 'All is lost, I am chased by the English', the *Spartak* fled at top speed, but the inexperienced crew could only get about 24-25 knots. At about 1330, blast from the forward gun knocked down the charthouse, destroyed the charts and concussed the helmsman. In the confusion the ship then ran over a shoal and stripped her propellers. Helpless, she was boarded and captured by HMS *Vendetta* and towed back to Reval. To the British she was 'dreadfully dirty', but among the debris they found messages about a meeting with the cruiser *Oleg* and the *Avtroil*.

The British light cruisers and destroyers missed the *Oleg* but they found the *Avtroil* next day. The destroyer's topmast was knocked down by the first shots, and she promptly surrendered. The two ships were repaired and presented to the fledgling Estonian navy in January 1919. As the *Vambola* and *Lennuk* they served until 1933, and were then bought by the Peruvians and renamed *Almirante Villar* and *Almirante Guise*.

Two of the incomplete ships were completed in 1927-28 as the *Karl Liebknecht* and *Rykov*, and with the *Lenin* and *Trotsky* they formed the Type IV group in the Soviet navy. The four ships' Second World War careers are to be found under the entry *Karl Liebknecht* Class.

Displacement: 1260 tons (normal) *Length:* 98 m (321 ft 6 in) oa *Beam:* 9.34 m (30 ft 9 in) *Draught:* 3.9 m (12 ft 9 in) *Machinery:* 2-shaft AEG steam turbines, 31 500 shp=35 knots *Armament:* 4 4-in (102-mm) (4×1); 9 17.7-in (45-cm) torpedo tubes (3×3) *Crew:* 168

The five ships ordered from the Russian Shipbuilding Works at Reval were designed by Normand but had Parsons turbines. Four

were laid down in November 1913 and the *Fedor Stratilat* a month later.

Name	launched	completed
Avtroil	1/1915	8/1917
Gromonosets	11/1914	1916
Pryemislav	8/1915	1927
Bryachislav	8/1915	—
Fedor Stratilat	—	—

The *Avtroil*, as we have already seen, was captured by British light cruisers and destroyers off Reval on December 27, 1918. The *Bryachislav* was towed to Petrograd in February 1918 and scrapped incomplete in 1923, but the *Fedor Stratilat* was demolished on the slipway in February 1918. The remaining vessel was completed in 1927, and the class became the Type III group in the Soviet navy The following changes of name occurred: *Gromonosets* renamed *Isiaslav* on June 27, 1915, renamed *Karl Marx* in 1923; *Pryemislav* renamed *Kalinin* in 1927.

Displacement: 1354 tons (normal) *Length:* 107 m (351 ft 0 in) oa *Beam:* 9.5 m (31 ft 3 in) *Draught:* 4.9 m (16 ft 0 in) *Machinery:* 2-shaft Parsons steam turbines, 32 700 shp=35 knots *Armament:* 5 4-in (102-mm) (5×1); 9 17.7-in (45-cm) torpedo tubes *Crew:* 168

The last of the Baltic Fleet destroyers were nine ordered from the Ziese, Muhlgraben Works at Riga. They were laid down after the outbreak of war but none was completed. Their names were *Rymnik, Khios, Grengamn, Gogland, Kulm, Patras, Smolensk, Stirsuden,* and *Tenedos*. Four, *Grengamn, Gogland, Kulm, Patras,* were transferred to the metal works yard at Petrograd in 1916, but like the others, work stopped in September 1917 and they were demolished by 1922. The particulars of this class were very

similar to the others, but mine capacity was increased to 80.

The destroyers built in the Black Sea were generally similar. The first group was ordered in 1912-1913 from Baltic Metal Works, Saint Petersburg, but the material was assembled at the Cape Kherson yard, most being completed by 1916.

Name	completed
Bespokojny	10/1914
Bistry	1915
Derzhi	10/1914
Gnevny	10/1914
Gromki	1916
Pospesny	1916
Pronzitelny	10/1914
Pylky	N/A
Shastlivy	N/A

The *Pospesny* was mined off Constanza in August 1916 but made harbour and was repaired. The *Gnevny* ran aground near Sevastopol on May 1, 1918 but was also repaired. the *Pronzitelny* and *Gromki* were scuttled on June 18, 1918, to prevent their capture by the Germans, but the *Shastlivy* fell into British hands in November 1918, and was scuttled in 1919 when the Anglo-French forces abandoned the Crimea. In 1920 the *Derzhy, Bespokojny, Gnevny, Pospesny* and *Pylky* were among the warships which carried White Russian refugees to Bizerta. There they rusted away through the 1920s and 1930s, being broken up by the French in lieu of money.

Only one of the class survived, the *Bistry*, which became the *Frunze* about 1921. She became the solitary Type II destroyer in the Soviet fleet and was sunk by German aircraft east of Tendra Island on September 21, 1941. She had been armed with a 75-mm AA gun, one 37-mm AA gun and two machine-guns. The twin torpedo tubes were replaced by three triple mountings before 1941 and when war broke out her speed had dropped to only 25 knots.

Displacement: 1110 tons (normal) *Length:* 93 m (305 ft 3 in) oa *Beam:* 9.3 m (30 ft 6 in) *Draught:* 2.8 m (9 ft 3 in) *Machinery:* 2-shaft Parsons steam turbines, 29 800 shp=32 knots *Armament:* 3 4-in (102-mm) (3×1); 10 17.7-in (45-cm) torpedo tubes (5×2) *Crew:* 160

Twelve destroyers of an enlarged design were ordered in 1915 from the Russian shipbuilding company at Nikolaiev, but only eight were laid down:

The Nikolaiev-built ships differed from the earlier Black Sea destroyers in having flat-sided or oval funnels, as against round. In other respects they were similar, apart from having triple torpedo tubes from the outset.

The *Feodonisi* was scuttled off Novorossiisk on June 18, 1918 with the *Gadjibey* and *Kaliakria,* while the *Kerch* was scuttled next day off Tuapse. The incomplete *Zerigo* was towed to Bizerta in 1920. The incomplete vessels were finished between 1923 and 1925 and became the Type VI group. Renamings were as follows:

Korfu renamed *Petrovsky* in 1923, renamed *Zhelezniakov* c1933;
Levkos renamed *Shaumyan* in 1925;
Zante renamed *Nvesamozhnik* in 1923.

The *Feodonisi* was refloated in the 1920s, and although the name *Khadyi* or *Vorovsky* was reported she was never repaired. The *Kaliakria*, however, was successfully salvaged in 1925 and recommissioned as the *Dzerzhinsky* in 1928.

See also *Artem* Class, *Dzerzhinsky* Class, *Gavriil* Class, *Karl Liebknecht* Class, *Kalinin* Class, *Frunze*.

Name	launched	completed
Kerch	1915	1916
Feodonisi	1915	1917
Gadjibey	1915	1917
Korfu	1916	—
Levkos	1916	—
Zante	1916	—
Zerigo	1916	—
Kaliakria	N/A	1918

Displacement: 1308 tons (normal) *Length:* 102 m (334 ft 9 in) oa *Beam:* 9.5 m (31 ft 3 in) *Draught:* 3 m (9 ft 9 in) *Machinery:* 2-shaft Parsons turbines, 32 500 shp=34 knots *Armament:* 4 4-in (102-mm) (4×1); 9 17.7-in (45-cm) torpedo tubes (3×3) *Crew:* 160

Azon

US guided bomb. Guided bombs aroused little enthusiasm among senior USAAF officers until August 25, 1943, when German aircraft were reported using guided bombs against shipping in the Bay of Biscay. Within weeks, radio-controlled Henschel Hs 293 rocket-boosted glide bombs and Fritz-X high-angle bombs had scored several hits on Allied shipping both in the Bay of Biscay and in the Mediterranean, including severe damage caused to the light cruiser USS *Savannah* and the battleship HMS *Warspite*.

This new development provoked immediate calls for an American equivalent. Although aeronautical and aerodynamic research were strictly the province of the National Advisory Committee for Aeronautics, the National Defense Research Committee carried out research into various subsidiary aspects of aerial warfare. A and D Divisions of the NDRC, already investigating guidance systems—some of which resulted in such variously successful missiles as the radar-guided Pelican, the television-equipped Roc and the heat-seeking Felix—were combined in Division 5 and this department produced the NDRC's most important and successful guided missile, the Azon.

Named from the fact that it could be steered in azimuth (horizontal plane) only, Azon consisted of a standard 454-kg (1000-lb)

general-purpose bomb fitted with a gyro stabilizer, radio receiver, steerable rudders and a tail flare to enable the controller to track the bomb in flight.

The bomb was originally designed in the summer of 1942, but before it could reach service there were several snags to be overcome. The main problem was the tendency of the bomb to spin in flight, thus negating the effect of the rudders and making the control system useless. It was not until May 1943, after Gulf Research and Development Laboratories had eradicated the faulty components and perfected the gyro stabilization, that Azon passed the critical test: of eight Azon and eight conventional bombs dropped simultaneously the average error of the uncontrolled bombs was 29 times that of the Azons.

The results of this test also overcame any official resistance to the bomb—a resistance which had rested largely on the fact that while guidance could not be proved to increase accuracy, it was obvious that having to prolong the bomb run until impact increased the risk to the crew of the launch aircraft.

There had been other objections, of course. One experienced USAAF officer claimed that no guided bomb could be of any use at all; others wanted to wait until Razon —which was to be steerable in both range and azimuth—became available. Razon, however, was not perfected in time to see service during the war, and was left behind by more sophisticated postwar developments.

Once in service, Azons were used to good effect by the USAAF in Europe, scoring hits on locks on the Danube, the Avisio viaduct in Italy and bridges over the Seine just before

Designed to be steerable in both range and azimuth, Razon was a more sophisticated version of Azon. Movable rudders, radio receiver and antennae and a gyro stabilizer added to a standard 1000-lb GP bomb formed a formidable guided weapon

the D-Day landings. Interest then appears to have lapsed, until early 1945 saw renewed use of the weapon, with spectacular results, against bridges in Burma.

On December 27, 1944, in Burma, three aircraft of 493 Squadron, 7th Bomb Group, attacked a three-span steel bridge with four Azon and four conventional bombs each. The conventional bombs all missed, but nine Azons dropped from the same height succeeded in destroying the centre span and damaging another.

During the next ten weeks, the 7th Bomb Group dropped 459 Azons, destroying 27 bridges in the process and scoring direct hits with 10-15% of the bombs dropped. Such success naturally gave rise to plans for more widespread use of the weapon, but these were abandoned with the end of the war.

Azor

Spanish torpedo boat class. Most steam torpedo boats were built by specialist builders in Britain, France and Germany. Spain bought some from all three countries, and in 1886 she acquired two, *Ariete* and *Rayo*, from the British firm of Thornycroft. In 1887 Yarrow built two more to almost identical dimensions and with the same armament for Spain at their Poplar works, and these were named *Azor* and *Halcon*.

Whereas the Thornycroft pair had a very short turtleback forecastle, three masts and two funnels placed one behind the other, *Azor* and her sister had a large turtleback forecastle, only two masts, and two funnels set side-by-side just behind the break of the forecastle. Two of the torpedo tubes were fitted alongside each other in the bow, and they carried a small davit to handle torpedoes on the fore end of the 'turtle deck'. A conning tower was built to the rear end of the forecastle, with a signal lamp mounted just in front of it.

They carried 25 tons of coal, and were intended for coast defence rather than extended operations. The accommodation was minimal, and the crew normally slept ashore, or in a depot ship. When the Spanish-American war broke out in 1898, *Azor* with *Ariete* and *Rayo* were hastily made ready to sail as reinforcements for the Spanish squadron in Cuba. However, the Spanish had not made any advanced preparations for the war, and the torpedo boats and their escort, *Ciudad de Cadiz*, only got as far as the Cape Verde Islands. They were in no fit state to undertake an ocean voyage and remained there until 1902, when they returned to Cadiz.

Both *Azor* and her sister were rebuilt in 1907. Their boilers were worn out, and were replaced with new Yarrow water-tube ones, and at the same time the twin funnels were replaced by a single stack. *Azor* sank after colliding with another torpedo boat, *Orion*, on exercises in Cadiz bay on April 8, 1911. One stoker was killed and eight injured. *Halcon* survived her by seven years.

Displacement: 108 tons (normal), 120 tons (full load) *Length:* 40.99 m (134 ft 6 in) *Beam:* 4.26 m (14 ft 0 in) *Draught:* 1.82 m (6 ft 0 in) *Machinery:* 1-shaft steam triple-expansion, 1600 bhp=24 knots *Armament:* 4 3-pdrs; 3 14-in (35.5-cm) torpedo tubes *Crew:* 23

B.1

B.1, first of the British 'B' Class submarines. Although none of the early Hollands had enough reserves of buoyancy or sufficient habitability to be useful for anything but coastal defence, Holland's ideas generally pointed the way towards modern submarine design—for example, the single shaft and the hydroplanes on the conning tower are now normal features

Cutaway illustration of the *B.11* as equipped with a sharpened steel wire-cutting device for her sortie up the Dardanelles. Sailing under the minefields she found the old Turkish cruiser *Messudieh* at anchor and sank her, an exploit which earned her captain the VC and provided the highlight of the 'B' Class's career

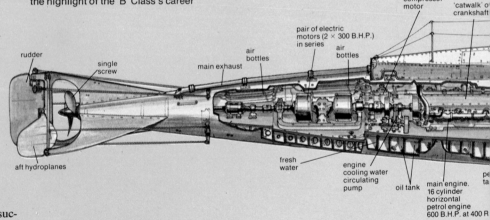

rudder

single screw

main exhaust

air bottles

pair of electric motors (2 × 300 B.H.P.) in series

air bottles

air compressor motor

'catwalk' o' crankshaft

aft hydroplanes

fresh water

engine cooling water circulating pump

oil tank

main engine. 16 cylinder horizontal petrol engine 600 B.H.P. at 400 R

pe ta

B.1

British submarine class. Following the success of the 'A' Class of 1903 the British Admiralty asked Vickers to build an improved model. The first was ordered as *A.14* but so many changes were made that the 11 boats were given B-numbers. The prototype, *B.1,* entered service late in 1904 and the last, *B.11,* joined the Fleet in 1906. Unlike other British submarines the forward pair of hydroplanes was positioned at the base of the conning tower.

As a class they were luckier than their predecessors, and only *B.2* was lost in a peace-time accident, being rammed in the Dover Straits on October 4, 1912 by the liner *Amerika.* They were still operational when war broke out in 1914, and three were stationed at Malta. When the Dardanelles campaign got under way these three boats were sent to Mudros and were reinforced by three more sent out from England. Their main task was to guard against a breakout by the German battlecruiser *Goeben,* but it was not long before someone thought of sending a submarine up the 27-mile long Narrows,

The British submarines *B.3,* *B.4* and *B.5* alongside the submarine depot ship HMS *Forth*

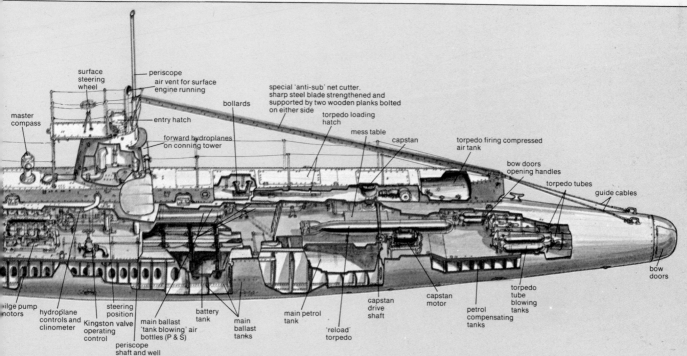

surface
steering
wheel

periscope
air vent for surface
engine running

master
compass

entry hatch

forward hydroplanes
on conning tower

bollards

special 'anti-sub' net cutter.
sharp steel blade strengthened and
supported by two wooden planks bolted
on either side

torpedo loading
hatch

mess table

capstan

torpedo firing compressed
air tank

bow doors
opening handles

torpedo tubes

guide cables

bow
doors

bilge pump
motors

hydroplane
controls and
clinometer

steering
position

Kingston valve
operating
control

periscope
shaft and well

main ballast
'tank blowing' air
bottles (P & S)

battery
tank

main
ballast
tanks

main petrol
tank

'reload'
torpedo

capstan
drive
shaft

capstan
motor

petrol
compensating
tanks

torpedo
tube
blowing
tanks

Plan of one of the 'B' Class submarines
converted to surface patrol vessels at Venice in
1915-16. The electric motors were removed, the
forward casing raised and a wheelhouse
provided in place of the conning tower.
Armament consisted of only a single 12-pdr, and
hardly justified the expense involved in the
conversion of the submarines

The Italian midget submarine *B.1* being readied for launching at Bari in mid-1916

similar to the prototype, the opportunity was taken to increase surface endurance to 209 km (130 miles) by fitting an Itala petrol motor. Like their predecessors they were designed by the distinguished naval architect, Lieutenant-General Edgardo Ferrati, and were built at the La Spezia arsenal.

Six of the *B* Class, numbered *B.1-6*, were ordered, two in July 1915 and four more in July 1916. However, *B.4-6* were stopped in 1917 when the steel shortage became acute. *B.1* was laid down in July 1915 and was launched complete on July 8, 1916. *B.2* was laid down in July 1915 and was launched complete on October 1, 1916. *B.3* was laid down in July 1916 and was launched complete on November 25, 1916.

under the five minefields which blocked the channel.

B.11 was chosen for the attempt, in preference to either of her sisters or the two French submarines present, because her batteries were in the best condition. Even so, it was asking a lot of an elderly, small submarine to face the 3-4 knot current which swept through the Narrows. She left on December 1, 1914 and after an exciting passage forced her way past the obstructions to find the old coast defence ship *Messudieh* lying at anchor. From a distance of 731 m (800 yards) Lieutenant Holbrook fired one 18-in torpedo, which hit and sank its 40-year-old target. For this exploit Holbrook was awarded the VC, but it was to be the only highlight of the 'B' Class's career.

At the end of 1915 the six boats were sent to Venice, where the Italians started to convert them to surface patrol craft. The electric motors were removed, the forward part of the casing was raised and the conning tower replaced by a wheelhouse. Armament was a single 12-pdr (3-in) gun, and it is questionable whether the expense was justified. *B.6-11* were renumbered *S.6-11* to indicate their changed status, but on August 9, 1916 *S.10* was sunk in dock at Venice by a bomb from an Austrian aircraft. She was the first submarine ever sunk by air attack. The others were commissioned about August 1917, and were sold at Malta in 1919 for scrapping. The five which remained in home waters served on local defence and were sold in 1919-21.

Displacement: 280/314 tons (surfaced/submerged) *Length:* 41.1 m (135 ft) oa *Beam:* 4.1 m (13 ft 6 in) *Draught:* 3 m (10 ft) *Machinery:* single-shaft petrol engine/electric motor, 600 bhp/190 hp=13/8½ knots (surfaced/submerged) *Armament:* 2 18-in (46-cm) torpedo tubes (forward) *Crew:* 16

B.1

Italian midget submarine class. Before the *A* Class midgets had been completed in 1915 the Italian navy ordered an improved version, to be called the *B* Class. Although basically

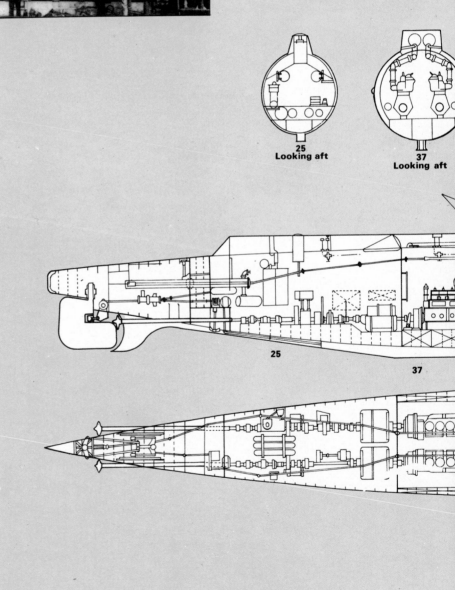

25
Looking aft

37
Looking aft

25

37

B.1 and B.2 were transported by rail to Bari, where they replaced A.2 and A.4 in defending the outer harbour. B.3 went to Venice at the end of 1917 but suffered continual mechanical problems and had to be paid off in June 1918. B.1-3 were discarded on January 23, 1919, together with the three incomplete hulls of B.4-6.

See also A.1 Class.

Displacement: 40/46 tonnes (surfaced/submerged) *Length:* 15.12 m (49 ft 7 in) oa *Beam:* 2.32 m (7ft 7 in) *Draught:* 2.56 m (8 ft 4½ in) *Machinery:* 1-shaft petrol motor, 85 bhp=6.9 knots (surfaced), 1 Savigliano electric motor, 40-60 hp=5 knots (submerged) *Armament:* 2 45-cm (17.7-in) torpedoes (external) *Crew:* 5

B.1

Norwegian submarine class. Six boats were projected for the Norwegian navy in 1914, based on an American Electric Boat company design, but they were not laid down until 1920 because of the difficulty of getting material from the USA during wartime. The boats were launched between 1923 and 1929, and the last was completed in 1930. Suller-type diesels were built under licence in Norway, as were the electric motors.

All six were scuttled at Horten when German forces invaded the country in April 1940, but B.1 was raised and towed to England. However, she did not play an active part in

Above: **Norwegian submarine B.6 at sea**

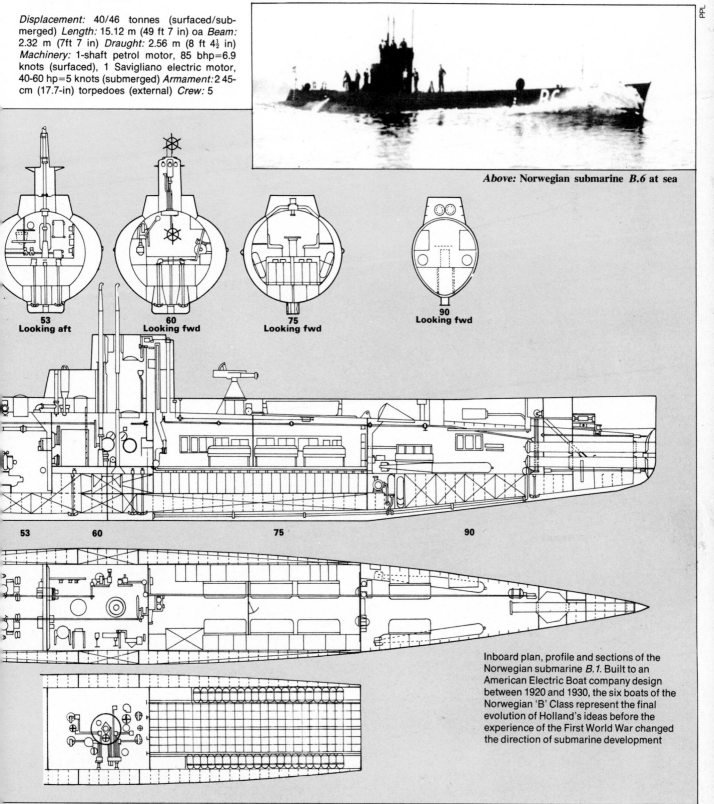

| 53 Looking aft | 60 Looking fwd | 75 Looking fwd | 90 Looking fwd |

Inboard plan, profile and sections of the Norwegian submarine *B.1.* Built to an American Electric Boat company design between 1920 and 1930, the six boats of the Norwegian 'B' Class represent the final evolution of Holland's ideas before the experience of the First World War changed the direction of submarine development

B-1 Rockwell International

the war, for lack of spares. She was returned in 1945 and subsequently stricken.

Displacement: 420/545 tons (surfaced/submerged) *Length:* 51.0 m (167 ft 4 in) oa *Beam:* 5.3 m (17 ft 6 in) *Draught:* 3.5 m (11 ft 6 in) *Machinery:* 900 bhp/700 hp=$15\frac{3}{4}$ knots/8.9 knots (surfaced/submerged) *Armament:* 1 3-in (76-mm); 4 18-in (46-cm) torpedo tubes *Crew:* 23

B-1 Rockwell International

American strategic bomber. No aircraft in history has ever been planned with such care as the B-1, nor over anything even approaching so long a period. Indeed one of its early forms, AMSA, was said to get its designation from 'America's most studied aircraft'—and that was back in 1963. In 1976, 14 years later, three B-1 prototypes were flying, but at the end of 1976 it was still impossible to predict whether or not the whole programme would be cancelled.

Without the B-1 the United States would be placed in a strategically almost impossible posture: the Soviet Union is becoming absolutely dominant in intercontinental missiles,

The first three prototype Rockwell B-1s photographed at Edwards Air Force Base in 1976

Rockwell International

and probably already has the capability to destroy virtually all the US strategic missile force at one blow, yet with no B-1 force an American president would not dare launch a retaliatory attack until the blow had actually fallen. Then it would be too late. With the B-1 many different options are possible, provided the aircraft can 'flush on warning'. Thus the crucial design characteristic was not great speed or altitude, as it had been with previous bombers, but the ability to take off, without fail, within 90 seconds of an alarm. Coupled with this is the capability to go on flying despite nearby thermonuclear explosions causing intense flash, electromagnetic pulse and similar effects.

To achieve the quick-start capability the crew can start all four engines simultaneously by hitting a button behind the nose landing gear as they run aboard. The extremely advanced General Electric F101 afterburning turbofans, each rated at 13 608 kg (30 000 lb) static thrust, have fixed inlets ahead of the long underwing ducts; originally fully modulated inlets were used, giving a Mach number at high altitude of about 2.2, but shortage of money has forced simplification, reducing the Mach number to 1.6. At takeoff the wings are fully spread, giving high lift with almost full-span flaps and slats.

Penetration of hostile airspace is rendered possible by the most comprehensive suite of defensive avionics ever installed in any aircraft, devised under the direction of Cutler-Hammer. So extensive are the avionics that

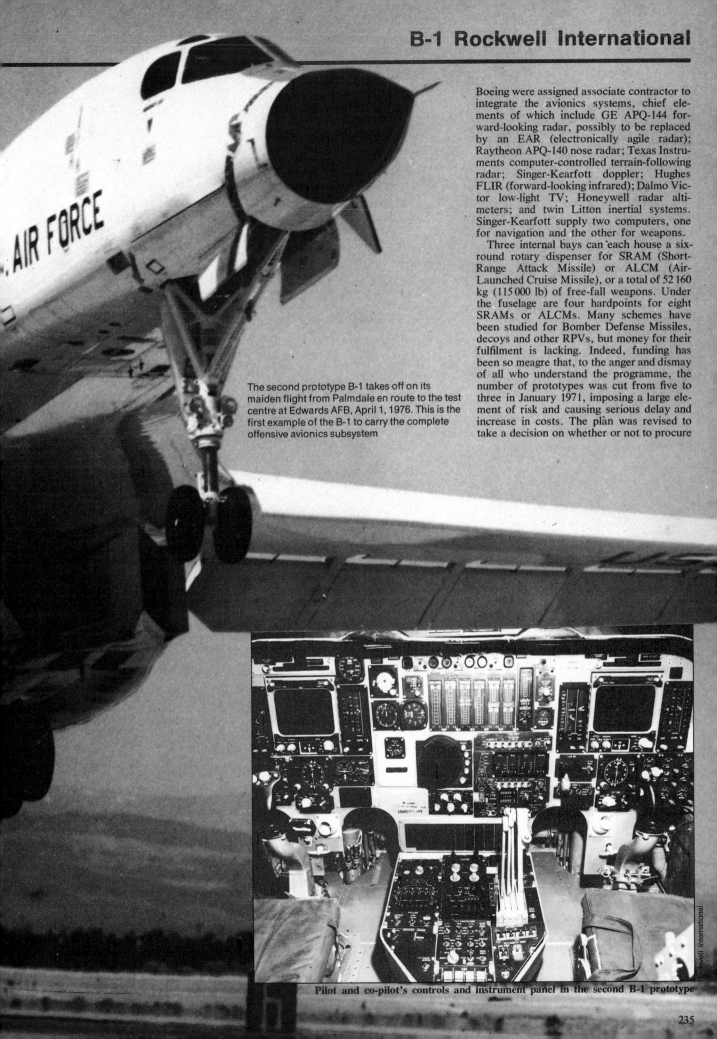

Boeing were assigned associate contractor to integrate the avionics systems, chief elements of which include GE APQ-144 forward-looking radar, possibly to be replaced by an EAR (electronically agile radar); Raytheon APQ-140 nose radar; Texas Instruments computer-controlled terrain-following radar; Singer-Kearfott doppler; Hughes FLIR (forward-looking infrared); Dalmo Victor low-light TV; Honeywell radar altimeters; and twin Litton inertial systems. Singer-Kearfott supply two computers, one for navigation and the other for weapons.

Three internal bays can each house a six-round rotary dispenser for SRAM (Short-Range Attack Missile) or ALCM (Air-Launched Cruise Missile), or a total of 52 160 kg (115 000 lb) of free-fall weapons. Under the fuselage are four hardpoints for eight SRAMs or ALCMs. Many schemes have been studied for Bomber Defense Missiles, decoys and other RPVs, but money for their fulfilment is lacking. Indeed, funding has been so meagre that, to the anger and dismay of all who understand the programme, the number of prototypes was cut from five to three in January 1971, imposing a large element of risk and causing serious delay and increase in costs. The plan was revised to take a decision on whether or not to procure

The second prototype B-1 takes off on its maiden flight from Palmdale en route to the test centre at Edwards AFB, April 1, 1976. This is the first example of the B-1 to carry the complete offensive avionics subsystem

Pilot and co-pilot's controls and instrument panel in the second B-1 prototype

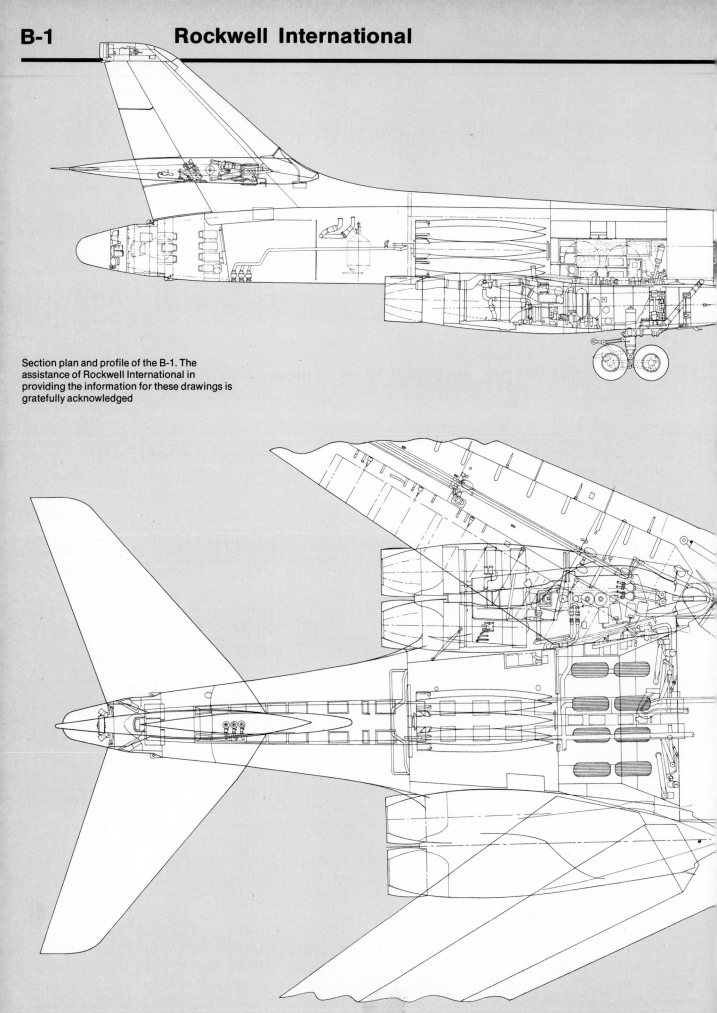

Section plan and profile of the B-1. The
assistance of Rockwell International in
providing the information for these drawings is
gratefully acknowledged

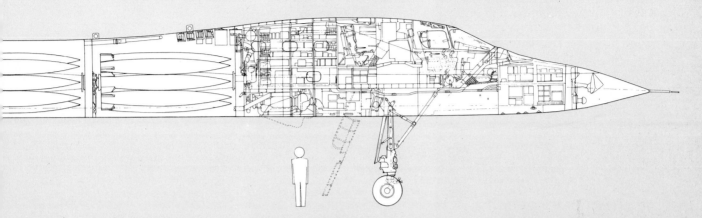

the B-1 for the USAF Strategic Air Command inventory after only 250 flight hours, which were exceeded in 1976. But the vital decision was postponed from November, immediately after the Presidential election, to March 1977.

The original plan was to buy a force of 241 aircraft, each costing an estimated $77 million allowing for R&D and inflation. This force seems a remote possibility, though the Soviet Union is almost certainly building a numerically larger force of Backfires. By late

The B-1's General Electric F101 turbofans were designed for variable geometry intakes; fixing the intakes to reduce costs reduced the bomber's maximum speed from Mach 2.2 to Mach 1.6

1976 the three prototypes had flown over 270 hours and reached beyond Mach 2.1 at 50 000 ft, but had been so constrained by funding that the test programme was a mere sampling process that concentrated on the design mission at Mach 0.85 at near sea level.

The fourth aircraft, ordered too late to be much help to the development programme, is to fly in February 1979 and from the start has

B.1 Sopwith

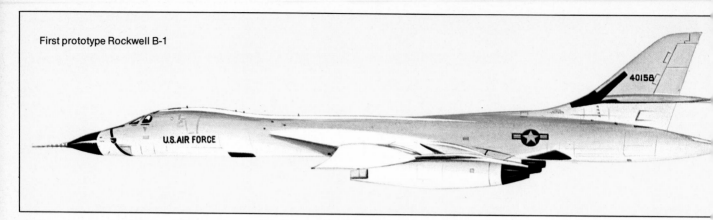

First prototype Rockwell B-1

been planned as virtually a production aircraft. It has the full defensive avionics and weapon capability, fixed inlets and other changes, including four ordinary ejection seats for the crew instead of a crew-escape capsule (another cost-saver). Should Congress at last appreciate the vital need for the B-1, the USAF will procure three aircraft with Fiscal Year 1977 funds and eight in the following year, building up to four aircraft a month by 1982.

Span: (spread at 15°) 41.7 m (136 ft 8½ in); (swept at 67½°) 23.84 m (78 ft 2½ in) *Length:* 45.8 m (150 ft 2½ in) *Designed takeoff weight:* 176 810 kg (389 800 lb) *Max speed:* (production aircraft) 1205 km/h (750 mph) at low level, Mach 1.6, or 1700 km/h (1056 mph) at altitude

B.1 Sopwith

British biplane bomber. Most Sopwith combat aircraft were fighters, but the B.1 was a true bomber, inspired by the success of the multirole 1½-Strutter as a single-seat bomber. Larger than the earlier machine, and almost twice as powerful with a 200-hp Hispano-Suiza water-cooled engine, the B.1 was a conventional single-seat biplane with four ailerons, and the prototype built in early 1917 demonstrated excellent handling qualities. No less than 254 kg (560 lb) of bombs could be carried in a vertical bay inside the fuselage aft of the cockpit. In addition to this load, exceptional for a small single-engined machine of 1917, a single 0.303-in Lewis machine-gun was synchronized to fire past the propeller blades.

Despite its weight—twice that of a Camel and 50% greater than a 1½-Strutter—the B.1's performance was satisfactory, and the bomb-

load caused no deterioration in handling. The Royal Naval Air Service 5th Wing at Dunkerque conducted operational trials, in the course of which actual missions were flown against the enemy. The evaluation was adverse, because with the bomb bay so far aft the B.1 was tail-heavy on the outward journey and tail-light flying back. Apparently it did not occur to anyone to transpose the bombs and cockpit.

Span: 11.73 m (38 ft 6 in) *Length:* 10.4 m (27 ft 0 in) *Gross weight:* 1377 kg (3035 lb) *Max speed:* not recorded, but about 185 km/h (115 mph)

B 1-6

Spanish submarine class. The six Spanish *B* Class submarines were an improved version of the *Isaac Peral,* which had been built for Spain at the Electric Boat Company's Fore River yard in the United States. Ordered under licence from the Electric Boat Company, *B 1-6* were built at Cartagena in Spain under the naval law of February 17, 1915. The first boat, *B 1,* was laid down in July 1916, and she was completed in June 1921. *B 2, B 3* and *B 4* were completed in 1922 and *B 5* and *B 6* in 1923.

Whereas *Isaac Peral* had all her torpedo tubes in the bow, *B 1-6* had only two in the bow and the other two in the stern. The 3-in AA gun was carried on a fixed mounting just forward of the conning tower. They were a standard medium-sized ocean-going submarine, with a radius of action on the surface of 12 875 km (8000 miles) at 10½ knots, and submerged of 200 km (125 miles) at 4½ knots. They were propelled on the surface by two sets of eight-cylinder Nelseco diesels, each of which developed 700 bhp, and they carried

66 tons of oil. On trials the class averaged 16.8 knots on the surface and 10.7 knots submerged. Two were based at Cartagena and four at El Ferrol, and it was off Cartagena in 1927 that *B 6* made a record dive which lasted for 72 hours.

By 1936, when the Spanish Civil War broke out, these submarines were already elderly, a submarine's normal active-service life lasting from ten to 15 years. However, they all saw active service on the Republican side. *B 6* was the first to be lost. She was caught and shelled on the surface by the Nationalist destroyer *Velasco* in September 1936 whilst on a voyage from Cartagena to Cantabrico. *B 4* and *B 5* were both sunk by aircraft, the former at Puerto Portman. *B 1* was damaged in a collision with a merchant

ship at Alicante in November 1937. Although the Republicans possessed 12 submarines at the outbreak of the war, they only played a small part in the fighting, and achieved very little. When the war ended in 1939 the surviving submarines were completely worn out. They were discarded in 1940 and 1941, but *B 2* was retained for use as a training vessel at the Escuela de Mecanicos. She was finally scrapped in 1952.

Displacement: 560 tons (surface), 830 tons (submerged) *Length:* 64.15 m (210 ft 6 in) *Beam:* 5.57 m (18 ft 4 in) *Draught:* 3.42 m (11 ft 3 in) *Machinery:* 2-shaft diesels, 1400 bhp=16 knots (surfaced), 2-shaft electric, 850 hp=10.5 knots (submerged) *Armament:* 1 3-in (76-mm) AA; 4 18-in (46-cm) torpedo tubes *Crew:* 28

The Sopwith B.1 single-engined bomber prototype photographed in 1918

John Taylor

B.1-20

Russian submarine class. In 1916 the Russian navy placed orders for 60 submarines for the Baltic Fleet, 28 of an improved Holland type based on the 'AG' Class, 7 Fiat type based on the Italian-built prototype *Sviatoi Georgi,* and 20 of an improved Bubnov type. Although work may have started on these vessels little progress had been made by the time the Revolution came, and the material was broken up on the stocks.

Little is known about the Bubnov-designed *B.1* Class: presumably they were similar to the *Bars* Class, but incorporating the improvements suggested by war experience. These would include raising the external drop collars to improve the handling of the boats, and more powerful machinery.

Displacement: 971/1264 tons (surfaced/submerged) *Dimensions:* unknown *Machinery:* diesel/electric, 17/9 knots (surfaced/submerged) *Armament:* 2 75-mm (3-in) guns; 2 machine-guns; 8 torpedo tubes (internal); 8 drop collars (external); 10 mines

Emperor Taisho's reign) in the old designation system. In the functional designation system it was the 2MT1 series.

A classic form of biplane, of wooden construction, the prototype was powered by a 450-hp Napier Lion W-type water-cooled engine and flew in January 1923. Military load comprised one 800-kg (1764-lb) torpedo or 485 kg (1070 lb) of bombs, whilst the observer had a 7.7-mm Lewis machine-gun in the rear cockpit. Most aircraft also had a fixed synchronized 7.7-mm Vickers. Between 1924 and 1933 no fewer than 442 of three main versions were delivered to the Imperial Navy, the B1M2 and B1M3 being powered by a 450-hp Mitsubishi HS12 (Hispano-Suiza licence) and the B1M3 being a three-seater. From 1927 the basic B1M was also built in

February 22, 1932 three B1M3s, escorted by three Type 13-2 fighters, together shot down a Chinese Boeing P-12 flown by an American, Robert Short. Most of this large family had been retired from active duty by 1938.

Span: 14.78 m (48 ft 5½ in) *Length:* 9.77 m (32 ft 0½ in) *Gross weight:* 2697 kg (5946 lb), (2MB1) 3300 kg (7278 lb) *Maximum speed:* 209 km/h (130 mph)

B-2 Curtiss

American heavy bomber. Having become an industrial giant in the First World War with patrol flying boats and the JN (Jenny) series of trainers, the Curtiss Aeroplane & Motor

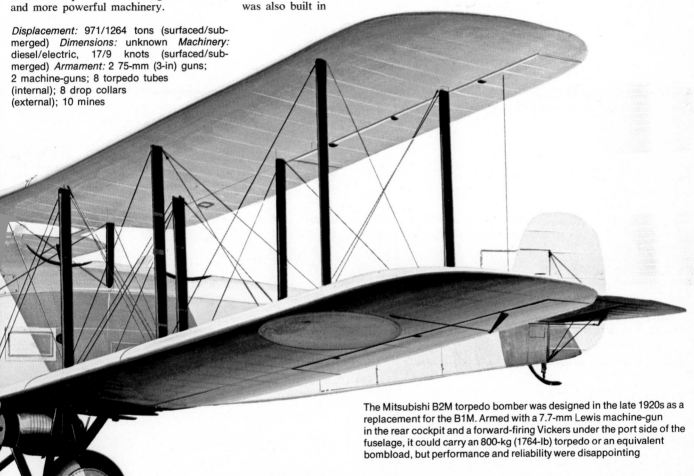

The Mitsubishi B2M torpedo bomber was designed in the late 1920s as a replacement for the B1M. Armed with a 7.7-mm Lewis machine-gun in the rear cockpit and a forward-firing Vickers under the port side of the fuselage, it could carry an 800-kg (1764-lb) torpedo or an equivalent bombload, but performance and reliability were disappointing

B1M Mitsubishi

Japanese carrier-based biplane bomber. One of the most important Japanese aircraft of the interwar period, the B1M was the last type designed at Nagoya by the team led by Herbert Smith, formerly of the Sopwith Company. Designed to meet a difficult specification for torpedo and bombing attack and reconnaissance, whilst operating from Japan's new aircraft carriers, the B1M was Type 13 to the Imperial Navy (13th year of

quantity (48) for the Imperial Army as the Type 87 (Japanese calendar year 2587) light bomber; this had the Mitsubishi designation 2MB1. A proportion of the final navy model, the B1M3, were manufactured by Hiro naval arsenal.

A further development was the 2MT4 Ohtori (Phoenix) of 1925, evaluated by the Imperial Navy as a float-seaplane for reconnaissance duties. It was not selected for production, but during 1926-29 Mitsubishi's Nagoya plant built 115 of a final sub-type, the 2MT5 Tora (Tiger), or Type 13-2 Model 2, which was a standard reconnaissance seaplane until the Second World War. The B1M saw a great deal of combat duty, and during the Shanghai Incident was involved in the first air combat by Japanese aircraft. On

Company won an important contract in 1921 when it underbid Martin on the latter's own MB-2 heavy bomber, 50 being delivered as Curtiss NBS-1. At the conclusion of this welcome batch Curtiss developed the design in two prototypes designated XNBS-4. In 1927 a further development resulted in the XB-2 Condor, which introduced a fuselage of welded steel tube. An extremely large biplane, in comparison with other Army Air Corps bombers of 1927, the XB-2 was powered by two 600-hp Curtiss Conqueror V-1570 water-cooled engines in large nacelles in the rear of which were gunners with paired machine-guns (usually 0.30-in Lewis, though the Marlin and Browning were also in service). Two more Lewis guns, making six in all, were aimed by a gunner in the nose. The

B2M Mitsubishi

bombload, carried internally and externally, was 1814 kg (4000 lb), considerably greater than that of any rival bomber, and the all-round performance was excellent. The Army evaluated the big Curtiss in September 1927, and eventually chose the Keystone XLB-6 which was cheaper and fitted the Army's hangars. But the XB-2 was so outstanding that in 1928 a production batch of 12 was ordered as the B-2. They were delivered in 1929-30, and saw combat duty. From them Curtiss developed the AT-32/BT-32 Condor.

Span: 27.43 m (90 ft 0 in) *Length:* 14.48 m (47 ft 6 in) *Gross weight:* 7492 kg (16 516 lb) *Max speed:* 212 km/h (132 mph)

B2M Mitsubishi

Japanese torpedo bomber. In 1927 the Imperial Navy issued a requirement for an all-metal replacement for the ubiquitous Mitsubishi B1M series of carrier-based bombers. Mitsubishi proposed three designs, all by British teams: the 3MR3, powered by the 650-hp Armstrong Siddeley Leopard radial (designed by Herbert Smith's team); 3MR4, powered by the 600-hp Mitsubishi Hispano-Suiza (Blackburn design under G E Petty); and the 3MR5, with the same Mitsubishi V-12 engine but rated at 650-hp (Handley Page design under George Volkert). Mitsubishi submitted only the 3MR4, and accordingly this was accepted by the navy, and a Blackburn-built prototype was delivered in February 1930.

Petty came to supervise Mitsubishi's production, and after technical snags with two further prototypes the fourth achieved all the required performance figures and entered production in March 1932 as the B2M1, Type 89-1. In general the B2M was very similar to the B1M, apart from its method of construction, and it carried the same armament and had a similar performance. Production was completed at 204 aircraft in 1935, the final

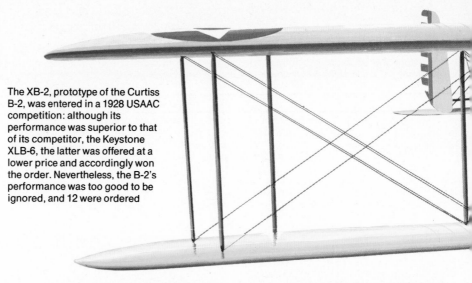

The XB-2, prototype of the Curtiss B-2, was entered in a 1928 USAAC competition: although its performance was superior to that of its competitor, the Keystone XLB-6, the latter was offered at a lower price and accordingly won the order. Nevertheless, the B-2's performance was too good to be ignored, and 12 were ordered

batch being of the modified B2M2 (Type 89-2) type in an attempt to reduce unserviceability. All B2Ms had three seats, with the observer/gunner in the rearmost cockpit. They were robust machines, with four ailerons and leading-edge slats. A number were still in service in 1940.

Span: 15.22 m (49 ft 11¼ in) *Length:* 10.27 m (33 ft 8¼ in) *Gross weight:* 3600 kg (7937 lb) *Max speed:* 213 km/h (132 mph)

B3 Gourdou-Leseurre

French fighter. In the years following the First World War, C E P Gourdou and J A Leseurre continued the development of their excellent wartime fighters (of which the 2.C1 was the last and best) and produced a series of technically interesting machines of exceptional performance, one of which, powered by one of the first Gnome-Rhône licence-built Jupiter engines, gained a world absolute

speed record at 360 km/h (224 mph). Their postwar fighters were based on an experimental machine called Type B constructed in 1918. Like most of the GL designs it was a parasol monoplane of advanced part-light-alloy construction.

Most of the subsequent products were experimental machines or racers, but in 1923 the B3 (type GL 22) was built and flown to meet a market for advanced trainers and light fighters for export outside France. Derived from the B2 fighter/racer and the navy ET, the B3 was a neat braced parasol monoplane with a 180/190-hp Hispano-Suiza 8Ac V-8 water-cooled engine and two synchronized machine-guns (usually 7.7-mm Vickers) above the front fuselage. In 1924-25 about 50 were delivered to the air forces of Czechoslovakia, Finland and Estonia, and the ZMAJ works in Yugoslavia built the B3 under licence. The B3 proved to be robust and thoroughly satisfactory, and one was in use as a civil aerobatic machine in Czecho-

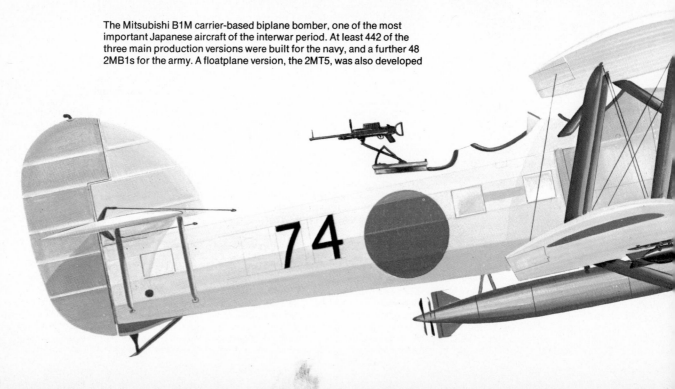

The Mitsubishi B1M carrier-based biplane bomber, one of the most important Japanese aircraft of the interwar period. At least 442 of the three main production versions were built for the navy, and a further 48 2MB1s for the army. A floatplane version, the 2MT5, was also developed

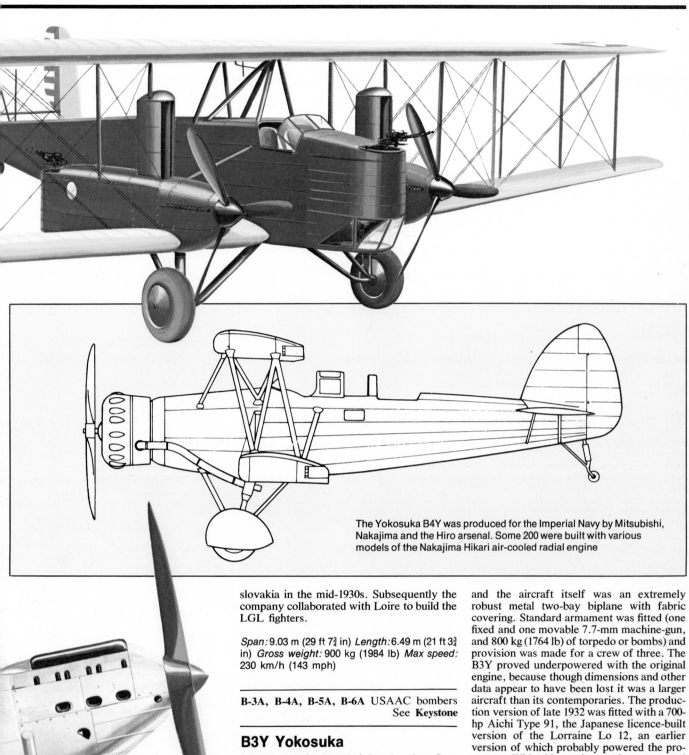

The Yokosuka B4Y was produced for the Imperial Navy by Mitsubishi, Nakajima and the Hiro arsenal. Some 200 were built with various models of the Nakajima Hikari air-cooled radial engine

slovakia in the mid-1930s. Subsequently the company collaborated with Loire to build the LGL fighters.

Span: 9.03 m (29 ft 7¾ in) *Length:* 6.49 m (21 ft 3¾ in) *Gross weight:* 900 kg (1984 lb) *Max speed:* 230 km/h (143 mph)

B-3A, B-4A, B-5A, B-6A USAAC bombers
See **Keystone**

B3Y Yokosuka

Japanese carrier-based biplane bomber. Contrary to the practice in other countries, the large air depots of the Imperial Japanese Army and Navy, whose primary purpose was aircraft distribution, modification and repair, in 1925-45 also undertook the design and construction of aircraft. Most important of these depots was the navy's Dai-Ichi Kaigun Koku Gijitsusho (1st Naval Air Technical Arsenal) at Yokosuka.

The B3Y was planned as a more modern replacement for the B1M family (notwithstanding the prior existence of the B2M) and the prototype is believed to have flown in 1930. The engine was a 500-hp V-12 water-cooled (the type appears to be unrecorded),

and the aircraft itself was an extremely robust metal two-bay biplane with fabric covering. Standard armament was fitted (one fixed and one movable 7.7-mm machine-gun, and 800 kg (1764 lb) of torpedo or bombs) and provision was made for a crew of three. The B3Y proved underpowered with the original engine, because though dimensions and other data appear to have been lost it was a larger aircraft than its contemporaries. The production version of late 1932 was fitted with a 700-hp Aichi Type 91, the Japanese licence-built version of the Lorraine Lo 12, an earlier version of which probably powered the prototype. With this engine performance and range were satisfactory, but production machines, designated Yokosuka Type 92, proved unreliable and cumbersome inside carrier hangars on account of their dimensions. Most or all of the 130 delivered were built by Aichi. Combat duty was relatively brief. No data available.

B4Y Yokosuka

Japanese carrier-based bomber. The inadequacies of the B3Y, which were self-evident by 1934, caused the Imperial Navy to issue an urgent 9-Shi specification for a new carrier-based attack aircraft in that year. (Shi num-

B5M Mitsubishi

bers were experimental numbers assigned to new projects with the numeral indicating the year of the Emperor's reign; thus, 1934 was the ninth year of Hirohito's reign.) The winner of the three designs submitted was the B4Y, designed under Sanae Kawasaki at the Yokosuka arsenal (see B3Y entry for background), making maximum use of existing airframe parts, including the outstandingly efficient wings of the Kawanishi E7K, and with the ability to accept almost any engine of suitable power.

The B4Y1 prototype had a 600-hp Hiro (arsenal) Type 91 water-cooled V-12, and was flown in 1935. A big and capable three-seater, it had spatted mainwheels with plenty of room between them for a torpedo, a very tall steerable tailwheel, and the folding wings of the E7K with four ailerons but no slats. Various radial engines were fitted to four more prototypes in 1936, as a result of which the B4Y1 went into production in November 1936 powered by the 840-hp Nakajima Hikari 2, nine-cylinder radial. Service designation was Type 96 carrier attack bomber. By 1938 Nakajima had delivered 37, Mitsubishi 135 and Hiro arsenal 28, a total of 200. These excellent machines saw action from carriers during the Sino-Japanese war, but were relegated to training in 1940, their place being taken by the B5N.

The B4Y was the subject of more than the usual amount of rumour. Several standard works claim that the Nakajima B4N won the 9-Shi competition, and that it was 'handed over to Yokosuka for completion', being redesignated B4Y. And after the attack on Pearl Harbor the Type 96 was the only Japanese torpedo bomber known to the Allies, so it was given the code name Jean, and frequently reported in action. It was even credited with sinking the British capital ships *Prince of Wales* and *Repulse*. In fact no B4Y was in combat service after early 1940.

Span: 15.0 m (49 ft 2½ in) *Length:* 10.15 m (33 ft 3½ in) *Gross weight:* 3600 kg (7937 lb) *Max speed:* 278 km/h (173 mph)

B5M Mitsubishi

Japanese carrier-based bomber. Designed to the same 10-Shi specification as the Nakajima B5N, this machine had an even better take-off performance and appeared to pose less technical risk. Powered by a 1000-hp Mitsubishi Kinsei 43 14-cylinder radial, the B5M had three seats under a long canopy, manually folding wings with slotted flaps, and an exceptionally large vertical tail and mainwheel spats. It carried the specified load of one 800-kg (1764-lb) torpedo or the same weight of bombs, plus a 7.7-mm machine-gun aimed by the observer. The Imperial Navy preferred the B5N, but the B5M was also put into production as an insurance against trouble with the technically advanced Nakajima aircraft. In the event no serious problems were encountered with the B5N, and manufacture of the B5M was halted after 125 had been delivered in 1937-38 as the Type 97 Model 2. The B5M saw service in both the Sino-Japanese and Second World Wars, usually operating from land airstrips, but never received an Allied code name.

Span: 15.3 m (50 ft 2½ in) *Length:* 10.234 m (33 ft 7 in) *Gross weight:* 4000 kg (8818 lb) *Max speed:* 381 km/h (237 mph)

B5N Nakajima

Japanese carrier-based torpedo bomber. This effective aircraft was no more than a synthesis of new developments pioneered in the United States, yet it was markedly superior to its counterparts in the US Navy (or anywhere else) and gave the Allies as nasty a shock as did the Zero, in the months following Pearl Harbor. The new developments included modern radial-engine cowling, variable-pitch propeller, retractable carrier-stressed landing gear, integral tankage, Fowler flaps, stressed-skin construction and mechanically folding wings, plus clean aerodynamic form—none revolutionary, but

The Nakajima B5N2 spearheaded the torpedo attack on the US fleet at Pearl Harbor, and went on to take part in most of the major carrier battles in the Pacific

An advance on the B5N, the Nakajima B6N1 was in most respects superior to the contemporary Grumman TBF Avenger and Fairey Barracuda, though the Mamori II engine gave a great deal of trouble and was replaced in the B6N2 by a Mitsubishi Kasei 25

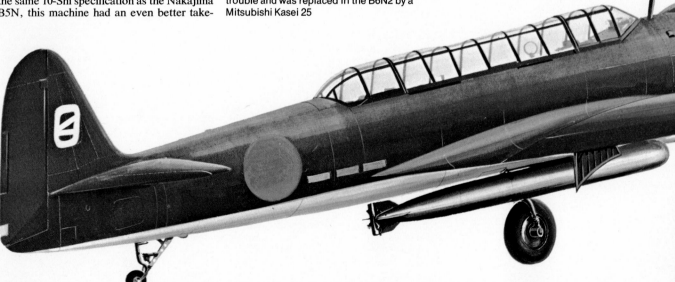

a marked contrast to the Douglas TBD and Fairey Swordfish.

The prototype B5N1, designed to a 1935 specification of the Imperial Navy for a carrier-based attack aircraft, flew on a 770-hp Nakajima Hikari 3, and carried a single 7.7-mm machine-gun in the rearmost of the three cockpits. Production aircraft, delivered from the end of 1937, were generally similar apart from being simplified by having plain slotted flaps and manually folding wings. The Model 12 had the 985-hp Sakae 11 engine, and in December 1939 the Model 23 (B5N2) followed with the 1115-hp Sakae 21 engine, crutches for a 800-kg (1764-lb) torpedo and enhanced armament of two fixed and either

one or two manually aimed machine-guns.

Altogether about 1250 B5Ns of all models were built by late 1942, when the B6N replaced what had become an obsolescent aircraft in the Nakajima plants at Handa and Koizumi. But in the first year of the Pacific war the B5N1 and B5N2 wrought more havoc on Allied vessels than any other single Japanese weapon. At Pearl Harbor the B5N scored torpedo hits on the battleships *Arizona* and *Oklahoma,* and in subsequent actions these aircraft—which received the Allied code-name of 'Kate'—were responsible for sinking the precious US carriers *Lexington, Wasp, Hornet* and *Yorktown.* A few surviving B5Ns were used as kamikaze aircraft in the final stages of the war.

Span: 15.52 m (50 ft 11 in) *Length:* 10.30 m (33 ft 9½ in) *Gross weight:* (B5N2) 4100 kg (9039 lb) *Max speed:* 378 km/h (235 mph)

B6N Nakajima

Japanese torpedo bomber. As with the B5N, the B6N was a triumph of ordinary aircraft design; it was at least as formidable as the much more complex and more costly Grumman TBF, and was greatly superior to the British Barracuda.

Like its predecessor the B6N was a clean and simple low-wing machine with a radial engine. In the B6N1 Model 11, first flown in March 1942, the engine was the 1870-hp Nakajima Mamoru, but this promising engine vibrated and overheated and had to be replaced in the B6N2 Model 12 by the well-tried 1850-hp Mitsubishi Kasei 25, which was also somewhat lighter and easier to maintain. In both installations the oil cooler was offset to the left to clear the 800-kg (1764-lb) torpedo. Dorsal and ventral 7.7-mm machine-guns were carried for rear defence, and in the B6N2 a third was fixed in the left wing.

The type was named Tenzan (heavenly mountain, a deified mountain in China), and after its first action against a US task group in the Marshalls in December 1943 it was code-named 'Jill' by the Allies. Total production amounted to 1268, all but about 200 being B6N2s. This extremely efficient version was first in action in the Marianas in May-June 1944, and hundreds were encountered at Truk, Bougainville and Iwo Jima.

In the final nine months of the war the B6N2 appeared with ASV radar, mounting damaging attacks in March 1945 on the Allied naval concentrations gathering off Kyushu. From April until June 1945 these aircraft sustained an all-out kamikaze and torpédo campaign on all Allied surface forces, especially off Okinawa. Had the Imperial Navy not lost all its carriers and almost all its skilled aircrew the B6N—by 1945 not much less obsolescent than its predecessor—could still have inflicted severe damage on Allied shipping. On many occasions the B6N acted as a reconnaissance aircraft, despite the availability of the C6N expressly designed by Nakajima for that purpose.

Span: 14.90 m (48 ft 10½ in) *Length:* 10.86 m (35 ft 7½ in) *Gross weight:* 5650 kg (12 456 lb) *Max speed:* (B6N2) 482 km/h (299 mph)

B-7 Douglas

American bomber. After a long series of Martin, Curtiss, Huff-Daland and Keystone biplanes this trim machine was a dramatic

The Douglas XB-7, prototype of the USAAC's first monoplane bomber, first flew in 1930

B7A Aichi

change when it was tested at Wright Field in 1930. Though the four crew members had open cockpits, the 600-hp Curtiss Conqueror V-1570-25 engines were in streamlined cowlings under the monoplane gull wing, and the main landing gear retracted. The XB-7, which

was originally designed as a high-speed observation machine, proved to be 96 km/h (60 mph) faster than the latest Keystone bombers, and Douglas then delivered seven service-test YB-7s with 675-hp V-1570-27 engines. But by 1931 the type was eclipsed by the Boeing B-9 and no squadrons were formed.

Span: 19.89 m (65 ft 3 in) *Length:* 14.2 m (46 ft 7 in) *Gross weight:* 5070 kg (11 177 lb) *Max speed:* 293 km/h (182 mph)

B7A Aichi

Japanese torpedo and dive-bomber. Designed under chief engineer Norio Ozaki as a replacement for both the Yokosuka D4Y ('Judy') and Nakajima B6N ('Jill'), this potentially very important machine was intended to operate from a new class of large aircraft carriers and so was exempted from previous limitations on size. The chosen power plant was the advanced but troublesome 2000-hp Nakajima NK9 Homare 18-cylinder radial, and the inverted gull wing

carried wide-track landing gear and passed above a capacious internal weapons bay equipped to carry an 800-kg (1764-lb) torpedo or the same weight of bombs.

The first of nine B7A1 prototypes flew in May 1942, with a crew of two and armament of two fixed 20-mm Type 99 cannon and a manually aimed 7.92-mm Type 1 machine-gun. After persistent engine difficulties these aircraft demonstrated excellent performance and manoeuvrability, and in early 1944 the

B7A2, with an NK9C engine and a 13-mm gun in the rear cockpit, went into production as the Ryusei (Shooting Star) at both Aichi's Funakata plant and the 21st Naval Air Arsenal at Omura, near Sasebo.

Small numbers were met in action and were given the Allied code-name 'Grace', but by this stage in the war Japan had lost all her carriers and the B7A2 was unable to do more than make scattered missions (often of a kamikaze nature) from shore bases. In May

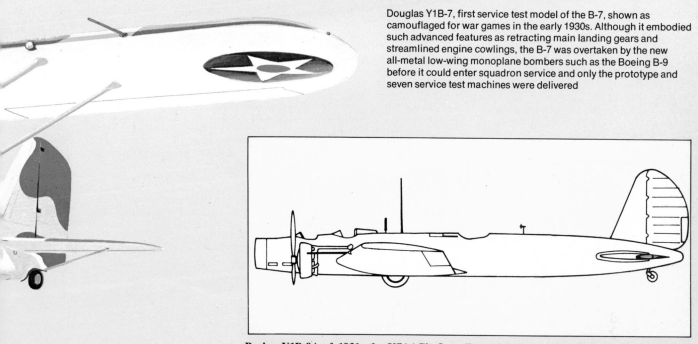

Douglas Y1B-7, first service test model of the B-7, shown as camouflaged for war games in the early 1930s. Although it embodied such advanced features as retracting main landing gears and streamlined engine cowlings, the B-7 was overtaken by the new all-metal low-wing monoplane bombers such as the Boeing B-9 before it could enter squadron service and only the prototype and seven service test machines were delivered

Boeing Y1B-9A of 1931, the USAAC's first all-metal bomber, embodied significant technical advances in aircraft construction. However, just as it had superseded the Douglas B-7, it was itself surpassed by the Martin Bomber, ordered as the B-10 and B-12

1945 an earthquake destroyed the Funakata factory, and by VJ Day total deliveries were only 80 by Aichi and 27 by Omura. The user squadrons were the Yokosuka and 752nd Kokutais.

Span: 14.4 m (47 ft 3 in) *Length:* 11.49 m (37 ft 8¼ in) *Gross weight:* 6500 kg (14 330 lb) *Max speed:* 566 km/h (352 mph)

B-9 Boeing

US Army bomber. Produced at a time when aircraft technology was rapidly developing beyond the standard of the First World War, the B-9 was significant technically but unimportant operationally.

In May 1930 Boeing flew the first Monomail civil mailplane, with all-metal stressed-skin construction, semi-retractable landing gear and cantilever monoplane wing of high

The Aichi B7A, designed for a projected new class of large aircraft carriers, was eventually built only in limited numbers

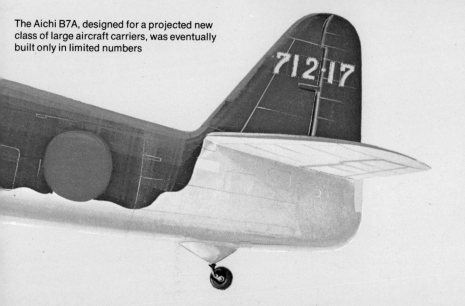

efficiency. With its own money it built the Model 214 bomber, scaled up to take two 600-hp Curtiss G1V-1570C water-cooled engines, and the Model 215, powered by 600-hp Pratt & Whitney Hornet radials. The latter flew on April 13, 1931, followed by the V-engined 214 on November 5 of that year.

The 215 became the YB-9 and its stablemate the Y1B-9. The Army Air Corps evaluation was favourable; performance exceeded that of available pursuits (fighters) and manoeuvrability was excellent. Up to four 0.5-in Brownings could be fitted to the nose and rear-dorsal gunner's cockpits, and two 499-kg (1100-lb) bombs could be carried externally. In 1932-33 Boeing delivered five service-test Y1B-9A bombers, with many changes including Y1GISR-1860B Hornets, revised vertical tail and four 272-kg (600-lb) bombs. Bulk orders, however, went to the Martin Bomber.

Span: 23.2 m or 23.42 m (76 ft or 76 ft 10 in) *Length:* 15.6 m or 15.85 m (51 ft 5 in or 52 ft) *Gross weight:* 6314 kg or 6495 kg (13 919 lb or 14 320 lb) *Max speed:* 302 km/h (188 mph)

Boeing Aerospace Company

B-18 Douglas

B-18 Douglas

US Army bomber (later, maritime patrol aircraft). In 1934 the US Army Air Corps invited proposals for a new bomber to replace the Martin B-10. Arthur E Raymond quickly designed the DB-1 (Douglas Bomber 1), also called Model 280, and a prototype was flying early in 1935. Based on the DC-2, the DB-1 differed mainly in having a deep pot-belly accommodating a remarkable bombload of up to 2948 kg (6500 lb) in an internal bay. The DB-1 showed it could lift the load with ease during trials at Wright Field in August 1935. Engines were 930-hp Wright Cyclone R-1820-45 driving controllable-pitch Hamilton propellers.

Though the rival Boeing 299 (B-17) was the eventual long-term choice, the short-term decision was that the DB-1 was the best of three contenders (the third was Martin's), and an immediate order was placed for the unprecedented total of 133, designated B-18 and later unofficially dubbed the Bolo. The prototype became the first production machine, and the last of the batch was the first DB-2 with power-driven nose turret, though defensive armament remained only three 0.30-in machine-guns in nose, dorsal and ventral positions. In 1938-39 a further 217 aircraft were delivered designated B-18A, with completely redesigned nose, 1000-hp R-1820-53 engines and revised dorsal turret. As the standard heavy bomber they saw extensive service during the period 1936-41. In 1940 a further 20 B-18A-type aircraft were supplied to the Royal Canadian Air Force as the Digby I for maritime patrol duties. Most of those in US service were eventually converted for this role.

The B-18A was the type chosen for all the earliest trials of US air/surface radar at Boston, and 122 aircraft were converted to carry ASV radar as the B-18B in 1942. They were the first aircraft in the world equipped with centimetric air/ground radar with scanner enclosed in a radome. The B-18B was also the first carrier of MAD (magnetic-anomaly detection) gear, in an extended tailcone. Other examples served during the period 1941-43 as paratroop trainers.

Span: 27.28 m (89 ft 6 in) *Length:* 17.63 m (57 ft 10 in); (original B-18), 17.27 m (56 ft 8 in) *Gross weight:* 12552 kg (27673 lb); (original) 11793 kg (26000 lb) *Max speed:* 346 km/h (215 mph)

B-36 Convair

USAF strategic bomber. Faced with the possibility of a successful German invasion of Britain, the United States government saw that there might one day be a need for an aircraft capable of bombing German-held Europe from bases in North America. On April 11, 1941 the USAAF initiated a design competition for a bomber able to fly from a 5000-ft runway and deliver a 10000-lb bombload on a target 5000 miles away, returning non-stop. This was far beyond the capability of any aircraft then built, but several companies tendered.

Northrop submitted an all-wing design which became the B-35 and later the all-jet B-49, but the eventual winner of quantity production orders was Convair, whose Model 37 was on many counts the biggest military aeroplane of all time. Its design rested on the availability of 3000-hp engines, six of which were fitted inside the gigantic wing driving pusher propellers for peak wing efficiency. The final choice of engine was the 28-cylinder Pratt & Whitney R-4360 Wasp Major, and though this eventually delivered 3800 hp both the engine installation and the 19-ft Curtiss Electric propellers gave severe trouble for many years.

In November 1941 Convair received a $15 million contract for design, engineering and two flight prototypes designated XB-36, but due to higher priority of the B-24 and other programmes the first did not fly until August 8, 1946. The B-36 was continued after the Second World War as the primary long-range

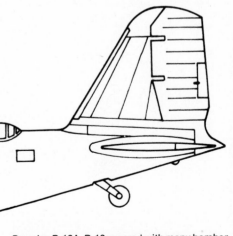

Douglas B-18A. B-18s served with many bomber units until they were replaced by B-17s on the outbreak of the Second World War

weapon of the new USAF Strategic Air Command. A production B-36A flew in August 1947 and the first major production sub-type, the B-36B, flew on July 8, 1948. This had bogie landing gears, pressurized compartments in the front, centre and rear fuselage linked by an 80-ft tunnel, a maximum bombload of 38 100 kg (84 000 lb) and defensive armament of 16 20-mm cannon in eight power-driven turrets. The B-36D was boosted by four 2360-kg (5200-lb) thrust GE J47 turbojets in twin pods under the outer wings, with inlet shutters to reduce drag when the jets were inoperative (their main purpose was to increase speed and height over the target), and the D was followed by the more powerful F, H and J with extra fuel, electronics and other changes. Total

deliveries to SAC amounted to 383, completed in August 1954.

Many B-36 variants were converted to RB-36 reconnaissance and electronic-warfare platforms, while others were used in Ficon (carriage of RF-84F reconnaissance fighter) and nuclear-propulsion experiments. The McDonnell XF-85 Goblin jet fighter was designed to be released from inside a B-36

RB-36D reconnaissance version of the Convair B-36 strategic bomber. Designed to deliver a 4535-kg (10 000-lb) bombload to a target 8000 km (5000 miles) away—ie, able to bomb targets in Europe from American bases in the event of a British surrender to Germany—the original six-engined giant had its power boosted by four turbojets in the D, H and J models

GRB-36D (the prefix indicated the parasite-carrier reconnaissance modification of the bomber), a B-36 adapted to launch a Republic F-84 Thunderjet which would make the final penetration on reconnaissance missions, returning to be retrieved by the carrier. Trials were successful, and some 12 B-36Ds underwent the modifications. Photo shows the swept-wing YF-84F on FICON (FIghter on CONvair) trials

B-135 Avia

but did not see active service. Several simulated 16000-km (10000-mile) missions were flown with heavy bombloads, but SAC never used the B-36 in action in Korea or elsewhere, withdrawing the last B-36 in February 1959.

Span: 70.1 m (230 ft 0 in) *Length:* 49.5 m (162 ft 1 in) *Gross weight:* (B-36J) 185 970 kg (410 000 lb) *Max speed:* (B-36D, J) 676 km/h (420 mph)

B-47 Boeing USAF bomber   See **Stratojet**

B-50 Boeing USAF bomber   See **Superfortress**

B-52 Boeing USAF bomber See **Stratofortress**

B-57 Martin USAF version of English Electric Canberra bomber See **Night Intruder**

B-58 Convair USAF bomber   See **Hustler**

B-66 Douglas USAF bomber   See **Destroyer**

B 71 Avia Czech bomber   See **SB-2 Tupolev**

B-135 Avia

Czech fighter. In 1937, following the great success of his B-34 (534) series of biplane fighters, Avia's brilliant designer, Frantisek Nowotny, planned a cantilever monoplane fighter, to have retractable landing gear and be powered by the new Avia 12Y-1000C liquid-cooled engine developed from Hispano designs to deliver 1000 hp. The prototype, however, had to make do with the 860-hp Hispano-Suiza 12 Ydrs, and a fixed, spatted landing gear. Designated Av-35-1, it flew in September 1938 and not only reached a speed of 494 km/h (307 mph) but also displayed outstandingly good handling. Of mixed steel-tube, aluminium, wood and fabric construction, it had an elliptical wing and enclosed cockpit.

After flying two more development aircraft the definitive B-135 (Av-135) flew in 1939. By this time the programme was in German hands, but work was instructed to continue. In 1941 a batch of 12 B-135 fighters were supplied to the Bulgarian air force, which originally intended to build the type under licence. Standard armament was one 20-mm Oerlikon cannon firing through the propeller hub and two 7.92-mm Mk 30 machine-guns in the top cowling. The engine was the 890-hp Avia HS 12 Ycrs.

Span: 10.85 m (35 ft 7 in) *Length:* 8.5 m (27 ft 10¾ in) *Gross weight:* 2462 kg (5428 lb) *Max speed:* 534 km/h (332 mph)

B-534 Avia

Czech biplane fighter. In 1930 the designers Benes and Hajn left Avia and were replaced by Frantisek Nowotny. He at once set about the priority task of designing a new single-seat fighter. From the Ba 33 he quickly developed a completely new machine, the B-34, flown in late 1931. A trim biplane of steel-tube construction, with mixed fabric and light-alloy covering, the B-34 was powered by the 650-hp Avia Vr 36 water-cooled V-12. Limited production was undertaken for the Czech government, while prototypes were

built with different engines. In August 1933 the B-534-I reached 365 km/h (227 mph), but with further refinement the B-534-II attained the excellent speed of 395 km/h (245 mph). Large orders were placed for the Czech army air force.

The standard engine was the Avia-built HS 12 Ydrs, rated at 860 hp. Early 534-II batches had an open cockpit and four 7.92-mm Mk 30 guns in the fuselage and lower wings. The -III had an enclosed cockpit and all its guns in the sides of the fuselage, the belt feeds having prominent blister fairings. The -IV had spats. One batch of 35 were fitted with 20-mm Oerlikon cannon and designated Bk-534. When the Germans occupied Bohemia-Moravia in March 1939 the B-534 force was more powerful than the fighter arm of the Luftwaffe. At least 445 entered service, and the majority were used by the Luftwaffe as trainers and tugs for gliders and targets. Three Slovak squadrons of B-534s served on the Russian front, but many pilots defected to join Czech units of the Russian air force.

Span: 9.40 m (30 ft 10 in) *Length:* 8.10 m (26 ft 7 in) *Gross weight:* 1980 kg (4364 lb) *Max speed:* 395 km/h (245 mph)

Ba 27 Breda

Italian single-seat fighter. Like Italian aviation generally in the period between the World Wars, the Società Italiana Ernesto Breda produced a succession of seemingly outstanding machines, which were demonstrated with great dash at air shows and often captured official records, but whose subsequent operational careers were dismal. One such machine was the Ba 27, and the same can be said of the company's subsequent major types, the Ba 65 and Ba 88 Lince.

The prototype Ba 27, obviously strongly influenced by the American Boeing P-26, was claimed to have performance unrivalled in Europe when it first flew in 1935. Compared with the American fighter it had slightly greater power, with a 660-hp Alfa-Romeo Mercurius IV (licence-built Bristol Mercury) nine-cylinder radial, and its public appearances left no doubt about its exceptional power of manoeuvre. But the type was not adopted by the Regia Aeronautica, and may well have been handicapped by shortcomings which were not immediately obvious. Breda had sent a strong team with the Italian government air mission to China in 1935, and this returned with a small order (believed to number 24 aircraft) for the Ba 27. These were duly delivered by sea during 1936 and were fully established in service in the Shanghai-Nanking district at the start of the Sino-Japanese war in July 1937. Their subsequent career was not distinguished. Armament comprised two 7.7-mm Breda-SAFAT machine-guns in the fuselage top decking.

Span: 9.48 m (31 ft 1 in) *Length:* 7.6 m (24 ft 11 in) *Gross weight:* 1786 kg (3938 lb) *Max speed:* 380 km/h (236 mph)

Ba 65 Breda

Italian attack bomber. The only one of Breda's many designs to see widespread operational service, this aircraft somehow contrived to be 145 mph slower than a Spitfire whilst having the same size, weight and power. It was extremely small for its role, and its one asset was a bombload and armament far greater than that of most aircraft of its day. The structure was curious, because a metal covering was used on a basic skeleton of welded steel tubing. Landing gears partially retracted rearwards into clumsy 'bathtubs' and there were no fewer than six struts to brace the tailplane. The engine was a 900-hp Isotta-Fraschini K-14 (Gnome-Rhône licence), 1000-hp Fiat A80RC41 or 1000-hp Piaggio P.XIRC40. Most Breda 65s were two-seaters, with the rear cockpit fitted with a 7.7-mm Breda-SAFAT machine-gun. The final variant, the Ba 65bis, had a rear turret armed with a 12.7-mm gun of the same make.

The prototype flew in 1935. Its remarkable bombload, alleged to comprise various combinations weighing up to 907 kg (2000 lb), plus a fixed wing armament of two 12.7-mm and two 7.7-mm Breda-SAFAT machine-guns, made up for a poor performance and manoeuvrability, and in 1937 the first batch equipped No 5 Sqn, Royal Iraqi Air Force. In August 1937 the first of 154 supplied to the Aviazione Legionaria (Italian air force in Spain) saw action, fighting with the Nationalists, but only in the reconnaissance role (the

John Taylor

Breda Ba 65bis with 12.7-mm machine-gun in hydraulically operated dorsal turret

inability to fly the designed mission has not been explained). By 1940, several hundred had been built, and had been exported to Hungary, Portugal and Paraguay.

Span: 12.1 m (39 ft 8 in) (some, 11.9 m) *Length:* 9.60 m (31 ft 6 in) *Gross weight:* 2950 kg (6505 lb) *Max speed:* 362 km/h (225 mph)

'Babs' Code name for Japanese reconnaissance aircraft   See **Ki-15 Mitsubishi**

Baby, Sopwith

British multi-role float seaplane. At the outbreak of the First World War the Sopwith Company's Tabloid and Schneider were among the most useful designs in existence as a basis for combat aircraft. They were extremely small and had outstanding power of manoeuvre, good pilot view and record-breaking performance. They were especially in demand as floatplanes (the Schneider version), and these were among the earliest military aircraft delivered in quantity, in 1914-15. Gradually performance fell, as more and more equipment and stores were loaded into these small and originally very light machines, and Sopwith rectified the matter by installing the more powerful 110-hp Clerget engine, in a conventional cowling open at the bottom (instead of an enclosed cowl with a pointed edge along the front).

The new aircraft, the Baby, had a longer fuselage and considerably greater gross weight, with increased fuel capacity and armament of two 29.5-kg (65-lb) bombs, Ranken darts, Le Prieur rockets and a 0.303-in Lewis machine-gun either firing obliquely up through a square aperture in the upper wing or synchronized to fire ahead. During 1915-17 some 457 Babies were delivered, many subtypes being produced by Sopwith, Blackburn, Fairey and Parnall. After the first batches the standard engine became the 130-hp Clerget. Fairey machines were so different they were called Hamble Babys, with thicker wings with full-flaps, improved floats, an angular (Campania-type) fin and other changes. Some were converted with wheel/skid land undercarriages. Babys flew antisubmarine, anti-Zeppelin, bombing, reconnaissance and fighting patrols from the North Sea to Palestine. They operated both from seaplane stations and from virtually all the early aircraft carriers.

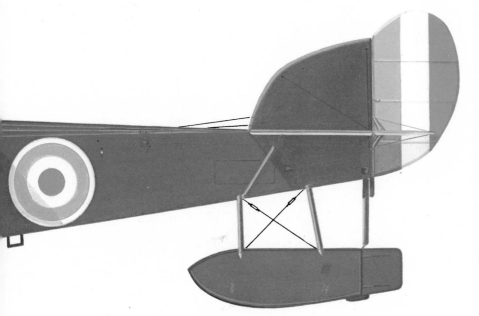

Sopwith Baby seaplane, developed from the earlier Schneider, powered by a 110-hp Clerget engine and armed with a single Lewis gun. Babys equipped most of the early aircraft carriers as well as operating from seaplane stations. The normal bombload of two 29-kg (65-lb) bombs, plus the gun ammunition, added to a pigeon, emergency rations and a sea anchor, made it somewhat overloaded, and later models were produced by Fairey and Blackburn with 130-hp Clergets

Span: 7.82 m (25 ft 8 in) *Length:* 7.01 m (23 ft 0 in) *Gross weight:* 778 kg (1715 lb) *Max speed:* 161 km/h (100 mph)

BAC British aircraft See **Canberra, Jet Provost, Lightning, Strikemaster**

Bachem German aircraft   See **Natter**

Backfin, Tupolev Tu-98

Backfin, Tupolev Tu-98

Soviet experimental bomber/interceptor aircraft. Backfin's role has been a subject of speculation since evidence of the type's existence reached the West in 1957. At first it was reported as a Yakovlev design, the Yak-42, and more recently the aircraft has been described variously as an experimental modification of the Tu-16 Badger, to test design aspects being developed for the Tu-28 Fiddler and as an unsuccessful competitor for the Yak-28 Brewer.

Backfin, which made its first flight in 1955 or 1956, had a fuselage generally similar to that of the Tu-16. The wing was mounted in a lower position, however, and shoulder-mounted air intakes above the wing fed the twin Lyulka AL-7F afterburning turbojets mounted side by side in the fuselage. The thrust from each engine was about 6000 kg (13 200 lb) dry and 10 000 kg (22 000 lb) with afterburning. RATO (rocket-assisted takeoff) was also used.

All undercarriage units retracted into the fuselage—an unusual feature for Tupolev designs of the time—and a small bomb bay was also let into the belly. Possible offensive armament, had the type entered service, has been reported as including air-to-air missiles.

Max speed (estimated): 1240 km/h (770 mph)

Backfire Tupolev

Soviet strategic reconnaissance bomber. The only large strategic attack aircraft in quantity production in the world today, this impressive aircraft is already in service in considerable numbers (by modern standards) and gives the Soviet Union a vital capability of launching an attack on mere warning, a response impossible with missiles. It also confers an extremely powerful capability against shipping in the open ocean, and can fly every kind of electronic and multi-sensor reconnaissance mission. Its development and large-scale production underscore the Soviet Union's ability to commit funds for weapons on a scale that would be extremely difficult in the West.

Existence of the Backfire was to be expected, because the Soviet Union's largest aircraft design bureau, that named after Andrei N Tupolev, did not produce a very useful aircraft in the Tu-22, given the NATO code name of Blinder. The original Backfire prototypes were virtually Tu-22 aircraft with variable-sweep outer wings, with pivots just

Plan, front and profile views of the Tupolev Backfire, based on available information

John Taylor

One of the few photographs of the Backfire, this one a Backfire-B

outboard of the large trailing-edge fairings for the bogie landing gears. They were rather larger, however, than the Tu-22, and almost certainly had larger engines and greater fuel capacity.

At least two prototypes were built, their existence being acknowledged in 1969. One was seen on the ground (presumably by reconnaissance satellite) at the Tupolev Kazan establishment in July 1970. About 12 development aircraft followed, all delivered before 1973, and these made many very impressive flights. After an observed flight-refuelling, one remained in the air a further ten hours, and several aircraft were engaged in tests with large missiles. At the same time it is extremely unlikely that the desired design performance was reached; published figures for the Tupolev bureau's performance objectives include over-target Mach number of 2.25-2.5 and unrefuelled range of 4775-5200 nautical miles (8850-9650 km).

American appreciations of the aircraft, known only by its NATO reporting name, indicated initial operational deployment in 1974 and the capability to act as a peripheral and intercontinental bomber, posing a threat to the United States itself when deployed with a compatible tanker force. During 1975 it was established that an improved model was in production, known as Backfire B (the original type becoming Backfire A). The new aircraft, which has been in production since 1974, has extended swing-wings and a completely new set of main landing gears which do not require the trailing-edge fairings (believed to have caused high drag at transonic and supersonic speeds). By 1976 there was evidence that its service designation was Tu-26, but the bureau designation (about 140) remained unknown.

Backfire B is a fine-looking aircraft, much larger than the Tu-22 but bearing an obvious family likeness. Engines are almost certainly closely related to those of the Tu-144 civil transport, which are Kuznetsov NK-144 afterburning turbofans each rated at 20 000 kg (44 090 lb) static thrust. Unlike the Tu-22 they are installed in extremely large rectangular-section trunks on each side, giving the fuselage a very broad shape similar to that of the

A-5 Vigilante of 1958. Even Backfire B still has only the outer portions of its wings swinging, and their range of movement is quite modest, the fully-swept shape closely resembling the wing planform of the Tu-22.

The greatly increased engine thrust and more efficient spread outer wings (which are believed to be fitted with slats), compared with the earlier aircraft, enable gross weight to be increased by almost 50%. Unrefuelled range is probably approximately tripled to about 11 265 km (7000 miles), but payload is modest at around 13 600 kg (30 000 lb). Various free-fall bombs and missiles can be carried, including a small weapon similar to the USAF SRAM and a very large stand-off missile code-named AS-6, with high-altitude

range estimated at 740 km (460 miles), one of which can be carried on a pylon under each wing at the pivot point. Often only one is carried, and accuracy is reported to be extremely precise.

There is abundant evidence that these aircraft are equipped from stem to stern with electronic and other countermeasures. Flight refuelling is accomplished with a large fixed nose probe, above the pointed nose radar. Production rate is estimated at five per month, with 110 of the B sub-type in operational service by the end of 1976. All are assumed to be on the strength of ADD (*Aviatsiya Dal'nevo Deistvaya*, or Long-Range Aviation), though a large proportion of the Tu-22 force were assigned to the AV-MF (*Aviatsiya Voenno-morskovo Flota*, or Naval Aviation). Western sources have guessed that the Soviet Union intends to deploy a force of 275 of these formidable aircraft. Soviet spokesmen insist that Backfire is 'tactical' and 'lacks intercontinental range', presumably in order to avoid limitation on its production under the terms of Strategic Arms Limitation agreements. Western experts consider such a claim to be demonstrably false.

(Estimated data) *Span:* 33.5 m (110 ft) spread, 26.8 m (88 ft) fully swept at about 55° *Length:* 41.2 m, (135 ft) *Gross weight:* 123 350 kg (272 000 lb) *Max speed:* (high altitude) about Mach 2.3, or 2445 km/h (1520 mph)

Baden

German battleship class. In 1910 work started on the design of a new class of battleships for the German navy, intended to outclass anything that the British might build. For many years German designers had chosen the 11-in gun in preference to the 12-in calibre favoured elsewhere, on the grounds that a

The German battleship SMS *Baden* returning from Heligoland in 1918

Bundesarchiv

light shell fired at high velocity was more effective than a heavier shell, but when the British moved to 13.5-in the Germans reluctantly followed by going up to 12-in. Experience was to show that the theory about light shells was fallacious, as the heavy, low-velocity shell favoured by the British had better ballistics, and so it was decided to adopt a calibre which would put the Germans ahead of their competitors for the first time. Unfortunately, just as the Germans came to the conclusion that they needed a 38-cm (15-in) gun the British embarked on their own 15-in Mk I programme.

The British could build ships faster than the Germans, with the result that when the *Baden* and *Bayern* commissioned after the Battle of Jutland the Royal Navy already had ten ships with 15-in guns in service. By a strange process both countries' designers had achieved very similar results, and the *Baden* Class bore a striking resemblance to the *Revenge* Class; both classes displaced 28000 tons and had eight 15-in guns, with the same scale of protection.

The *Baden* became Fleet Flagship in October 1916. The *Bayern* was still on trials at the time of Jutland but took part in the Baltic operations, being mined on October 12. The *Baden* was not among the ships listed for surrender under the terms of the Armistice, but the *Mackensen* could not get to sea and so the *Baden* was substituted about two weeks late. Both ships were scuttled in Scapa Flow on June 21, 1919 but the *Baden* was beached by British boarding parties. The

Bayern was raised in September 1934 and scrapped at Rosyth; the *Sachsen* and *Württemberg* were scrapped at Kiel and Hamburg respectively in 1920-21.

The British now had the chance to run comparative trials on the latest example of German battleship design, and from July 1919 until early in 1921 the ship was measured, stripped and shot at to test every conceivable aspect of her construction. The conclusions were that she would have been too lively a gun-platform for the Atlantic, the guns, because of their low elevation, were outranged by the British 15-in, and the armour was below the specified British standard. Her protection was slightly heavier in some areas but lighter in others, and the percentage of armour to displacement was almost identical. This did much to dispel the myths about how vastly superior German designs were, but the fact remains that the *Baden* design was good, and it served as the basis for the *Bismarck* Class 20 years later.

The 38-cm/L45 had a maximum range of 20297 m (22200 yards) at 16° elevation, whereas the 15-in/42-cal Mk I had a range of 22220 m (24300 yards) with 20° elevation. Moreover, the British shell weighed 871 kg

(1920 lb) as against 750 kg (1653 lb) for the German shell, which made it more accurate at extreme ranges.

After being fired at by the 15-in guns of the monitors *Erebus* and *Terror*, which fired 31 shells into chosen parts of the hull and superstrucure, the *Baden* had bombs of various sizes detonated on her decks. Finally, she was used as a target for a full-calibre shoot by the battleships of the Atlantic Fleet southwest of Portsmouth and sank on August 16, 1921. The tests showed conclusively that if the new pattern 15-in shell had been available at Jutland the Germans almost certainly would have suffered heavier losses than those they incurred.

Displacement: 28600 tons (normal), 32200 tons (full load) *Length:* 190 m (623 ft) oa *Beam:* 30 m (98 ft 6 in) *Draught:* 8.6 m (27 ft 9 in) normal *Machinery:* 3-shaft steam turbines, 53000 shp=22.3 knots *Protection:* 349.4-171.6 mm (13¾-6¾ in) belt; 57.2-32.8 mm (2¼-1¼ in) decks; 349.4 mm (13¾ in) turrets *Armament:* 8 15-in 45-cal (4×2); 16 150-mm (5.9-in) 45-cal (16×1); 2 8.8-cm (3.5-in) AA (2×1); 5 60-cm (23.6-in) torpedo tubes (submerged, 1 bow, 4 broadside) *Crew:* 1171 (1271 as flagships)

Baden sinking after a pounding by British warships in 1921

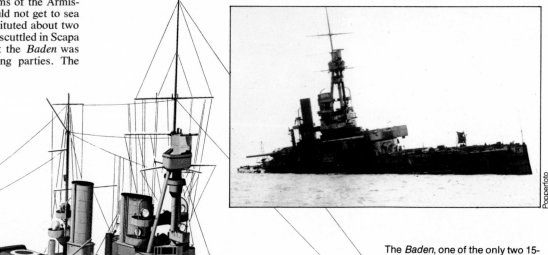

Popperfoto

The *Baden*, one of the only two 15-in gunned battleships built by Germany during the First World War. The roundels on the turrets are identification marks for aircraft

Name	laid down	launched	completed	built
Baden	1913	10/1915	10/1916	F Schichau, Danzig
Bayern	1914	2/1915	3/1916	Howaldt, Kiel
Württemberg	1914	6/1917	—	AG Vulcan, Hamburg
Sachsen	1914	11/1917	—	Germania Yard, Kiel

Royal Navy

MOD

Novosti

Top: A Badger-D electronic surveillance version of the Tu-16 flies over HMS *Ark Royal. Above left:* Badger-F, a maritime reconnaissance type with underwing electronic pods. *Above right:* Soviet airmen parade in front of their Badger-Bs armed with AS-1 Kennel antishipping missiles

Badger

Canadian flame-throwing tank. The first Badger was developed at the request of 1st Canadian Army and was no more than a Ram Kangaroo carrying the flame-throwing equipment of the Wasp Mk 2. The Ram Kangaroo was a de-turretted Ram tank converted into an armoured personnel carrier, while the Wasp was a 100-gallon (455-litre) flamethrower normally mounted in a Universal Carrier.

The marriage was successful: the Badgers were issued in February 1945 and were used by the Lake Superior Regiment during the attack on the Reichswald Forest known as Operation Veritable. Since the Ram Kangaroo had no overhead protection for the crew, a second Badger was then developed which used the standard Ram tank as its basis and mounted the flame gun in the turret in

place of the usual 6-pdr gun. These saw some action with 5th Canadian Armoured Brigade in the western Netherlands in April 1945.

At the end of the war the Badgers were scrapped, but in 1947, needing some flame tanks for experimental and training purposes, the Canadians converted three old Sherman tanks into Badgers by removing their turrets and fitting flame guns into the hull front plates. These were scrapped in the 1950s.

Badger, Tupolev Tu-16

Soviet strategic bomber, used more recently for reconnaissance and missile operations. The Badger, formerly designated Tu-88 and Samolet-N, was the Soviet Union's first long-range strategic jet bomber. About 2000 were built, the type making its first public appearance in 1954.

The ADD (*Aviatsiya Dal'nevo Deistvaya,*

or Long-range Aviation) of the Soviet air force still operates more than 500 Badgers, and about 300 serve with the AV-MF (*Aviatsiya Voenno-morskovo Flota,* or Naval Aviation). Early versions were supplied to Indonesia and Egypt; these fell into disrepair or were destroyed on the ground in the 1967 Six-Day war respectively. More recently Egypt has received the later Badger-G, and Iraq also operates the type. Some 60 Badgers have been built in China since 1968.

The Badger's oval fuselage accommodates a crew of seven, including two pilots, navigator and observer/rear gunner. The mid-mounted swept wing has two Mikulin AM-3M turbojets buried in its roots, with the nacelles partially faired into the fuselage to reduce drag. Early models were powered by engines of 8200-kg (18 000-lb) thrust, but installed power has been increased in stages to at least 9500 kg (21 000 lb). Fuel is carried

Baffin Blackburn

in the wing and fuselage, and aerial refuelling is carried out by the wingtip-to-wingtip method. The Tu-16 was developed into the Tu-104 airliner by fitting a new fuselage and mounting the wing in a lower position.

The original Badger-A strategic bomber can carry up to 9000 kg (20 000 lb) of weapons in the bomb bay. Defensive armament consists of seven 23-mm cannon: two each in a manned rear turret and unmanned barbettes under the rear fuselage and behind the cockpit, plus a single forward-firing weapon in the starboard side of the nose. Two observation blisters are mounted on the sides of the rear fuselage.

Badger-B, the only variant no longer operational, carried two AS-1 Kennel air-to-surface missiles on underwing pylons. This combination has since been superseded by Badger-Gs carrying AS-5 Kelts (see below). In the Badger-C variant a large search radar is installed in the nose, in addition to the mapping radar fitted under the chin. This model can carry the obsolescent AS-2 Kipper missile partially recessed in the forward part of the bomb bay.

The Badger-D is employed on maritime reconnaissance, having a nose radar similar to that installed in Badger-C. The chin radome is slightly larger than in previous versions, and three additional fairings are found under the fuselage. Badger-E carries cameras in its bomb bay, and Badger-F has electronic-countermeasures pods on pylons under each wing. Normal practice is for a Badger-F to operate in conjunction with a Tu-16 of a different variant.

The most recent model is the Badger-G. This has underwing pylons for two AS-5 Kelt air-to-surface missiles, and this aircraft/missile combination was used by the Egyptian air force against targets in Sinai during the October 1973 war. The Badger's intended replacement, the supersonic Tu-22 Blinder, is in fact only partially superseding its predecessor and the Tu-16 is likely to outlive the contemporary Royal Air Force V-bombers as well as the now-retired B-47 Stratojet.

Span: 33.5 m (110 ft) *Length:* 36.5 m (120 ft) *Gross weight:* 68 000 kg (150 000 lb) *Max speed:* 950 km/h (590 mph)

Baffin Blackburn

British torpedo bomber. Between the World Wars Blackburn Aircraft was responsible for many of the Royal Navy's carrier-based attack aircraft, a major type being the Ripon. In September 1933 this had been so developed that it was judged worthy of a new name, and Baffin was chosen.

The new machine met Specification 4/33, and it went into production with the Bristol Pegasus air-cooled radial of 565 hp. Previously the Ripon had been powered by the water-cooled Lion, and Ripon development aircraft had been tested with both a Pegasus and a two-row Tiger, both uncowled and with a Townend ring cowling. The Baffin entered service, with an uncowled engine, in No 812 Squadron in 1934.

Apart from being easier to look after and somewhat more reliable, the Baffin marked little advance over the Ripon. It carried the same load of pilot, observer, 715-kg (1576-lb) Mk VIII or Mk X torpedo or up to 907 kg

(2000 lb) of bombs, and one fixed Vickers 7.7-mm machine-gun and a manually aimed Lewis of the same calibre on a Fairey high-speed mounting.

Only 15 Baffins were ordered new by the Royal Navy, but Blackburn sold a batch to New Zealand and also received contracts to convert an eventual total of 60 Ripons to Baffin standard. In Britain the type was declared obsolete in 1937, but the RNZAF machines served until 1940.

Span: 13.86 m (45 ft 6 in) *Length:* 11.68 m (38 ft 4 in) *Gross weight:* 3452 kg (7610 lb) *Max speed:* 219 km/h (136 mph)

Bahia

Brazilian cruiser class. Under the 1907 Naval Programme the Brazilian navy ordered two scout cruisers from Armstrong–Whitworth, Elswick-on-Tyne. The two ships, *Bahia* and *Rio Grande do Sul*, followed contemporary British practice, with light guns disposed side by side on the forecastle, six sided in the waist a deck lower, and another pair side by side on the poop. Armour protection comprised a 1½-in arched steel deck over the machinery. In conception they were very like the same builders' *Adventure* and *Attentive* of 1903 but with more powerful machinery and 4.7-in guns in place of 4-in. Machinery was supplied by Vickers.

Neither ship saw any action, despite the fact that Brazil was involved peripherally in both World Wars. In 1925-26 both were refitted by the Companhia Nacional de Navigacao Costeira at Rio de Janeiro. When first completed they had only a foremast and two short funnels, but after 1926 they had a mainmast and taller funnels. The original Parsons turbines and Yarrow boilers were replaced by Brown-Curtis geared turbines and Thornycroft oil-burning boilers. As a result they were two knots faster than before. Another change was the provision of 21-in Bliss-Leavitt torpedoes in place of the original British-pattern 18-in.

The fire control originally comprised voice-tubes from the control stations to the bridge, and from there to a plotting room on the second deck. In 1925-26 director-control was installed, with a spotting position on the foremast. A rangefinder was provided over the charthouse and four searchlights.

Bahia was laid down in 1908, launched in January 1909, and completed in 1910. *Rio Grande do Sul* was laid down in 1908, launched in April 1909, and completed in 1910. The *Bahia* was discarded about 1944 and the *Rio Grande do Sul* in 1946.

Displacement: 3100 tons (normal) *Length:* 115.82 m (380 ft 0 in) *Beam:* 11.88 m (39 ft 0 in) *Draught:* 4.4 m (14 ft 6 in) mean *Machinery:* (as built) 3-shaft direct-drive steam turbines, 18 000 shp=26½ knots; (as rebuilt) 3-shaft geared turbines, 23 000 shp=28½ knots *Protection:* 37 mm (1½ in) deck; 76 mm (3 in) conning tower *Armament:* (as built) 10 4.7-in (120-mm)/50 cal (10×1); 6 47-mm (6×1); 2 45-cm (17.7-in) torpedo tubes, above water; (by 1945) 10 4.7-in; 4 3-in (76-mm) AA (4×1); 4 21-in (53-cm) torpedo tubes (above water) (2×2) *Crew:* 368

Bainbridge

US destroyer class. The first destroyers to be built for the US Navy were the 16 *Bainbridge* Class, authorized on May 4, 1898 and completed in 1902-3. They were part of the huge expansion of the Navy at the time of the war with Spain but they also marked the growing awareness inside and outside the Navy that it was no longer a coast defence force, and the fleet had to be protected on the high seas.

The new British torpedo boat destroyers (TBDs) were chosen as the model, but as in Britain and other countries the individual builders were given a free hand to meet a broad specification. As a result four separate types were built, all differing in some degree. The three private designs, by Harlan & Hollingsworth, the Fore River company and Maryland Steel had flush decks and 'turtleback' forecastles like original British '27-knotter' and '30-knotter' designs, but the official Navy Bureau of Construction and Repair design was more ambitious. They were given raised forecastles to provide a proper deck and better seakeeping. An important innovation in all four types was the provision of bilge keels to reduce the rolling.

During construction of the Navy-designed ships, tests were carried out at the new 'model basin' at Washington navy yard, and as a result their after hull-lines were altered. After ships had entered service it was found necessary to strengthen the conning tower forward against the shock of firing the 3-in gun overhead. Another improvement was the

Badger-A, initial production version of the Soviet Tu-16 medium strategic bomber, shown in the markings of the Egyptian air force. Badger-A can carry up to 9000 kg (20 000 lb) of weapons in the bomb bay, and is armed with seven 23-mm cannon, two in the tail, two each in remotely controlled barbettes below the rear fuselage and behind the cockpit and one in the starboard side of the nose

resiting of the galley in a small deckhouse. The Navy-designed destroyers turned out slightly slower than the private designs, but their improved hull design meant a more realistic sea speed, and they set the pattern for future development.

Nine of the Navy or *Bainbridge* type were built, followed by the *Hopkins* and *Hull* with less power and slightly smaller hulls, and the three *Truxtun* and two *Lawrence* types with larger hulls and more power. Although hull numbers were not officially adopted until 1920, for convenience these groups can be divided as follows: nine *Bainbridge*s num-

bered *DD.1-5* and *DD.10-13*, two *Hopkins* Type numbered *DD.6-7*, two *Lawrence*s numbered *DD.8-9* and three *Truxtun*s numbered *DD.14-16*. Appearance varied from builder to builder, much as it did in French and British destroyers of the day. The *Lawrence* and *Macdonough*, for example, had

Badger-E maritime reconnaissance aircraft, with camera equipment in their weapons bays, demonstrate their wingtip-to-wingtip flight refuelling

MOD

Bainbridge

their four funnels together while the *Hopkins* and *Truxtun* types could be distinguished by different heights and shapes of funnels, those of the *Hopkins* and *Hull* being oval in section, those of the *Truxton*, *Whipple* and *Worden* rounded.

In 1903 the new destroyers replaced the former torpedo flotilla, forming the 1st Flotilla; *Bainbridge*, *Barry*, *Chauncey*, *Dale* and *Decatur*. The 1st Flotilla made a 4-month, 15 000-mile voyage via the Suez Canal to the Asiatic Station. Several ran out of coal in mid-Atlantic and had to be refuelled by the tender *Buffalo*. In 1907-8 only six remained on the East Coast, *Hopkins*, *Hull*, *Lawrence*, *Stewart*, *Truxtun* and *Whipple*. They went with the Battle Fleet around Cape Horn to join the rest of the class on the Pacific coast. During the First World War they served on convoy escort, and on November 19, 1917, the *Chauncey* was rammed and sunk west of Gibraltar by the British merchantman *Rose*. Her captain and 20 crewmen were lost.

The surviving ships were all sold in 1920. The majority were scrapped but the *Truxtun*, *Whipple* and *Worden* were converted for mercantile use. After re-engining with diesels they were used as fast banana-carriers for many years. The *Truxtun* was lost on September 5, 1938, the *Worden* on May 1, 1947, and the *Whipple* was scrapped in 1956.

Name and No	launched	commissioned	builders
Bainbridge (DD.1)	8/1901	11/1902	Neafie & Levy, Philadelphia
Barry (DD.2)	3/1902	11/1902	Neafie & Levy, Philadelphia
Chauncey (DD.3)	10/1901	11/1902	Neafie & Levy, Philadelphia
Dale (DD.4)	7/1900	10/1902	Wm R Trigg Co, Richmond, Va
Decatur (DD.5)	9/1900	5/1902	Wm R Trigg Co, Richmond, Va
Hopkins (DD.6)	4/1902	9/1903	Harlan & Hollingsworth, Wilmington, Delaware
Hull (DD.7)	6/1902	5/1903	Harlan & Hollingsworth, Wilmington, Delaware
Lawrence (DD.8)	11/1900	4/1903	Fore River Engine Co, East Braintree, Mass
Macdonough (DD.9)	12/1900	9/1903	Fore River Engine Co, East Braintree, Mass
Paul Jones (DD.10)	6/1902	7/1902	Union Ironworks, San Francisco
Perry (DD.11)	10/1900	9/1902	Union Ironworks, San Francisco
Preble (DD.12)	3/1901	6/1902	Union Ironworks, San Francisco
Stewart (DD.13)	5/1902	12/1902	Gas Engine & Power Co & Chas L Seabury, New York
Truxtun (DD.14)	8/1901	9/1902	Maryland Steel Co, Sparrows Point, Md
Whipple (DD.15)	8/1901	10/1902	Maryland Steel Co, Sparrows Point, Md
Worden (DD.16)	8/1901	12/1902	Maryland Steel Co, Sparrows Point, Md

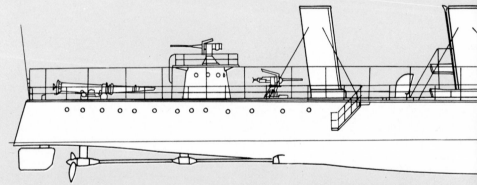

USS *Bainbridge*, name ship of the first class of destroyers in the US Navy. Armed with two 3-in quick-firers, five 6-pdrs and two 18-in torpedo tubes, they were modelled on contemporary British torpedo boat destroyers, though the four different builders involved were allowed considerable freedom in meeting the specification. The Navy types, of which *Bainbridge* was one, differed from the other designs in having raised, rather than turtleback, forecastles to improve sea-keeping

(DD.1-5, 10-13) *Displacement:* 420 tons (normal), 480 tons (full load) *Length:* 76.2 m (250 ft 0 in) oa *Beam:* 7.18 m (23 ft. 7¼ in) *Draught:* 1.97 m (6 ft 6 in) *Machinery:* 2-shaft vertical triple-expansion, 8000 ihp=28½ knots *Armament:* 2 3-in (76-mm) QF (2×1); 5 6-pdr (57-mm) (5×1); 2 18-in (46-cm) torpedo tubes *Crew:* 72

(DD.6-7) *Displacement:* 408 tons (normal) *Length:* 75.81 m (248 ft 9 in) *Beam:* 7.46 m (24 ft 6 in) *Draught:* 1.82 m (6 ft 0 in) *Machinery:* 2-shaft vertical triple-expansion, 7200 ihp=29 knots *Armament:* As above *Crew:* 72

(DD.8-9) *Displacement:* 446 tons (normal) *Length:* 74.98 m (246 ft 3 in) *Beam:* 6.77 m (22 ft 3 in) *Draught:* 2.05 m (6 ft 9 in) mean *Machinery:* 2-shaft vertical triple-expansion, 8400 ihp=29 knots (designed) *Armament:* As above *Crew:* 72

(DD.14-16) *Displacement:* 433 tons (normal) *Length:* 78.94 m (259 ft 6 in) *Beam:* 7.06 m (23 ft 2 in) *Draught:* 1.82 m (6 ft 0 in) *Machinery:* 2-shaft vertical triple-expansion, 8300 ihp=29½ knots *Armament:* As above+1 6-pdr *Crew:* 72

Bainbridge

US nuclear frigate. In Fiscal Year 1956 the US Navy was authorized to build its third nuclear-powered surface ship, as part of the programme to explore and develop the concept of an all-nuclear navy. The new ship was to be a 'destroyer-size' frigate armed with the latest surface-to-air missiles (DLGN) and was intended to act as an escort for the nuclear-powered carrier *Enterprise* (CVAN-65) and the cruiser *Long Beach* (CGN-9).

For a cost of $163 610 000 the US Navy got a 7600-ton ship armed with light guns, antiaircraft missiles and antisubmarine weapons. She is capable of almost indefinite cruising at high speed, and like the old sailing warships her endurance is limited only by the stores and fresh water carried. The D2G pressurized water-cooled nuclear plant was designed by the Atomic Energy Commission's Knolls Atomic Power Laboratory, and it comprises two reactors. They generate steam for twin-shaft geared turbines.

Armament is conventional, two twin Ter-

rier RIM-2 SAM launchers, one forward and one aft, an Asroc RUR-5A eight-tube launcher behind the forward Terrier launcher and two twin 3-in/50 cal automatic guns abreast of the after superstructure at forecastle deck level. These were added as an afterthought when it dawned on the USN that a ship like the *Bainbridge* had no close-range defence against 'soft' targets. Mark 10 Terrier launchers are carried, a Mod 5 type forward and a Mod 6 aft. Unofficial reports credit the ship with 40 Terrier rounds in each magazine. Two triple Mk 32 torpedo tubes are carried just forward of the boats amidships, and they fire Mk 44 or Mk 46 antisubmarine homing torpedoes.

The SQS-23 sonar is mounted in a massive bulbous bow. The Hughes SPS-52 3-D search radar aerial is carried on the foremast, with an SPS-10 on a lower platform and an SPS-37 search antenna on the mainmast. In late 1976 the *Bainbridge* completed a comprehensive overhaul of her antiaircraft capability, at Puget Sound naval shipyard. Known as an Anti-Air Warfare (AAW) fit, it began in June

Displacement: 7600 tons (normal), 8580 tons (full load) *Length:* 162.2 m (565 ft) oa *Beam:* 17.64 m (57 ft 10¾ in) *Draught:* 8.83 m (29 ft) *Machinery:* 2-shaft geared steam turbines, nuclear-fuelled, 60 000 shp=30 knots+ *Protection:* none *Armament:* 2 Terrier SAM launchers (2×2) (80 missiles); 1 Asroc ASW missile launcher (1×8); 2 triple 12.75-in (32.4-cm) torpedo tubes; 4 3-in (76-mm)/50-cal (2×2) *Crew:* 451

US Navy

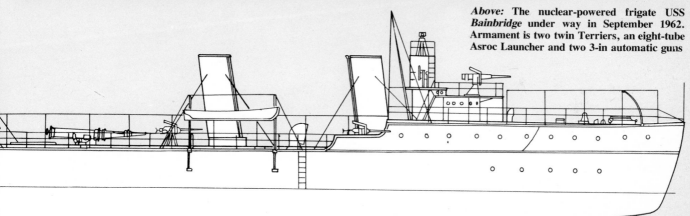

Above: The nuclear-powered frigate USS *Bainbridge* under way in September 1962. Armament is two twin Terriers, an eight-tube Asroc Launcher and two 3-in automatic guns

1974 and cost an estimated $103 million. She will probably have a mixture of Terrier and Standard missiles with improved guidance, and it is known that she will be equipped with the Naval Tactical Data System (NTDS).

The *Bainbridge* is basically an enlarged version of the conventional *Leahy* Class frigates, and looks similar apart from her heavy lattice masts. She was laid down on May 15, 1959, launched on April 15, 1961, commissioned on October 6, 1962 and allocated to the Pacific Fleet in 1965. She was built by Bethlehem Steel, Quincy, Mass.

See also Terrier RIM-2, Asroc.

Baka ('fool') Allied nickname for Japanese suicide bomb   See **MXY Yokosuka**

Balao

US submarine class. No class better demonstrates the US Navy's rational policy of speeding up and simplifying wartime ship-building. Following the construction of the successful *Gato* Class (itself only a repetition of a sound pre-war design) through 73 units, the decision was taken to increase diving depth and incorporate improvements suggested by war experience. To achieve this it was not necessary to do more than strengthen the hull of the *Gato* design, and so no external change was made apart from shifting the anchor to the port side and mounting the deck gun forward of the conning tower.

In fact, the first of the *Balao* Class were laid down and launched in 1942 before the last of the *Gatos*. The lead ship, *Balao*, was launched on October 27, 1942 at Portsmouth navy yard and commissioned on April 2, 1943. In all 132 boats were ordered from five shipyards, and only ten contracts were cancelled at the end of the war. From the *Clamagore* (SS.343) onwards the diesel/electric drive was changed, reduction gearing was done away with and the motors were coupled directly to the shafts to reduce noise.

The five builders involved were Portsmouth navy yard (SS.285-291, SS.308-312 and SS.381-410); Wm Cramp Shipbuilding, Philadelphia (SS.292-303); Mare Island navy yard, California (SS.304-307 and SS.411-416); Electric Boat company, Groton (SS.313-352 and SS.370-378); and Manitowoc (SS.361-369). The *Dugong* (SS.353) *Eel* (SS.354) and *Espada* (SS.355) were cancelled on October 23, 1944. *Jawfish* (ex-*Fanegal*, SS.356), *Ono* (ex-*Friar*, SS.357), *Garlopa* (SS.358), *Garrupa* (SS.359), *Goldring* (SS.360), *Needlefish* (SS.379) and *Nerka* (SS.380) were cancelled on July 29, 1944.

The *Balao* Class had as impressive a war record as the *Gatos*, and included many of the most successful US submarines of the Second World War. Probably the most outstanding feat was that of the *Archerfish* which sank the giant Japanese aircraft carrier *Shinano* while she was being moved from Yokosuka to the Inland Sea to complete fitting out.

In 1947-48 the *Carbonero* (SS.337) and *Cusk* (SS.348) became the first operational submarines fitted to fire guided missiles.

Left: The *Balao* Class submarine USS *Becuna* (SS.319) running on the surface

They were fitted with a watertight hangar and a ramp for launching a 'Loon', the American copy of the V-1 flying bomb.

Many of the class were modernized under the Guppy (Greater Underwater Propulsive Power) programme initiated at the end of the 1940s. This resulted in a total confusion of the *Balao* Class with the later *Tench* Class. The conversion included lengthening the hull to accommodate larger batteries, removing all deck guns and rebuilding the bow and conning tower (now called the 'sail') to provide faster underwater speed and less noise. As time progressed further improvements were incorporated, so that there were Guppy I, IA, II, IIA and III types. The following *Balao*s were converted:

Guppy IA—SS.319, SS.322-324, SS.341-342, SS.403, SS.406-407
Guppy IIA—SS.340, SS.365, SS.368, SS.377, SS.382, SS.391, SS.394, SS.396, SS.402, SS.410
Guppy II—SS.339, SS.347, SS.349-350, SS.352
Guppy III—SS.343-344, SS.346, SS.351

By the end of 1976 only one *Balao* Class remained in service with the USN, the transport submarine *Sealion* (LPSS.315). Ironically she was unmodernized, apart from having a widened casing to allow the launching of inflatable assault boats. She has the distinction of being the last Second World War submarine in the US Navy.

See also *Gato*, Guppy, Loon.

Displacement: (later boats) 1526/2424 tons (surfaced/submerged); (earlier boats) 2391-2414 tons submerged *Length:* 95.02 m (311 ft 9 in) oa *Beam:* 8.31 m (27 ft 3 in) *Draught:* 4.65 m (15 ft 3 in) *Machinery:* (surfaced) 2-shaft diesel 5400 bhp=20¼ knots; (submerged) 2-shaft electric, 2740 hp=8¾ knots *Armament:* 1 5-in (127-mm)/25-cal or 1 4-in (102-mm)/50-cal or 1 3-in (76-mm)/50-cal; 1 40-mm AA (some); 1 20-mm AA (some); 2 .5-in or .3-in mg; 10 21-in (53-cm) torpedo tubes (6 forward, 4 aft, 24 torpedoes carried) *Diving Depth:* 122 m (400 ft); SS.361-364 only 91.4 m (300 ft) *Crew:* 80-85

Hull no and name	launched	fate
SS.285 *Balao*	10/1942	Used as target 1964
SS.286 *Billfish*	11/1942	Scrapped 1971
SS.287 *Bowfin*	12/1942	Stricken 1971 and preserved as memorial
SS.288 *Cabrilla*	12/1942	Scrapped 1972
SS.289 *Capelin*	1/1943	War loss Dec 1943
SS.290 *Cisco*	12/1942	War loss Sep 1943
SS.291 *Crevalle*	2/1943	Scrapped 1971
SS.292 *Devilfish*	5/1943	Sunk as target 1968
SS.293 *Dragonet*	4/1943	Sunk as target 1961
SS.294 *Escolar*	4/1943	War loss Oct 1944
SS.295 *Hackleback*	5/1943	Scrapped 1968
SS.296 *Lancetfish*	8/1943	Accidentally lost 1945, scrapped 1959
SS.297 *Ling*	8/1943	Stricken 1971
SS.298 *Lionfish*	11/1943	Stricken 1971
SS.299 *Manta*	11/1943	Sunk as target 1969
SS.300 *Moray*	5/1944	Sunk as target 1970
SS.301 *Roncador*	5/1944	Stricken 1971
SS.302 *Sabalo*	6/1944	Stricken 1971
SS.303 *Sablefish*	6/1944	Scrapped 1971
SS.304 *Seahorse*	1/1943	Scrapped 1968/69
SS.305 *Skate*	3/1943	Used as target at Bikini 1946

Balao

Hull no and name	launched	fate
SS.306 *Tang*	8/1943	Sunk by own torpedo Oct 1944
SS.307 *Tilefish*	10/1943	Venezuelan *Carite* 1960
SS.308 *Apogon* (ex-*Abadejo*)	3/1943	Used as target at Bikini 1946
SS.309 *Aspro* (ex-*Acedia*)	4/1943	Sunk as target 1963
SS.310 *Batfish* (ex-*Acoupa*)	5/1943	Stricken 1969 and preserved as memorial
SS.311 *Archerfish*	5/1943	Sunk as target 1968
SS.312 *Burrfish* (ex-*Arnillo*)	6/1943	Canadian *Grilse* 1961-69
SS.313 *Perch*	9/1943	Stricken 1971
SS.314 *Shark*	10/1943	War loss Oct 1944
SS.315 *Sealion*	10/1943	Transport submarine, still in service 1976
SS.316 *Barbel*	11/1943	War loss Feb 1945
SS.317 *Barbero*	12/1943	Sunk as target 1964
SS.318 *Baya*	1/1944	Stricken 1972
SS.319 *Becuna*	1/1944	Stricken 1973
SS.320 *Bergall*	2/1944	Turkish *Turgut Reis* 1958
SS.321 *Besugo*	2/1944	Italian *Francesco Morosini* 1966
SS.322 *Blackfish*	3/1944	Stricken 1972
SS.323 *Caiman* (ex-*Blanquilla*)	3/1944	Stricken 1972
SS.324 *Blenny*	4/1944	Stricken 1973
SS.325 *Blower*	4/1944	Turkish *Dumlupinar* 1950
SS.326 *Blueback*	5/1944	Turkish *Ikinci Inonu* 1948
SS.327 *Boarfish*	5/1944	Turkish *Sakarya* 1948
SS.328 *Charr* (ex-*Boccaccio*)	5/1944	Stricken 1971
SS.329 *Chub* (ex-*Chubb*, ex-*Bonaci*)	6/1944	Turkish *Gür* 1948
SS.330 *Brill*	6/1944	Turkish *Birinci Inonu* 1948
SS.331 *Bugara*	7/1944	Accidentally lost 1971
SS.332 *Bullhead*	7/1944	War loss Aug 1945
SS.333 *Bumper*	8/1944	Turkish *Cannakale* 1950

Hull no and name	launched	fate
SS.334 *Cabezon*	8/1944	Sold 1971 for scrapping
SS.335 *Dentuda* (ex-*Capidoli*)	9/1944	Sold 1969 for scrapping
SS.336 *Capitaine*	10/1944	Italian *Alfredo Cappellini* 1966
SS.337 *Carbonero*	10/1944	Stricken 1970
SS.338 *Carp*	11/1944	Stricken 1971
SS.339 *Catfish*	11/1944	Argentine *Santa Fe* 1971
SS.340 *Entemedor* (ex-*Chickwick*)	12/1944	Turkish *Preveze* 1972
SS.341 *Chivo*	1/1945	Argentine *Santiago del Estero* 1971
SS.342 *Chopper*	2/1945	Stricken 1971
SS.343 *Clamagore*	2/1945	Stricken 1974
SS.344 *Cobbler*	4/1945	Turkish *Canakkale* 1973
SS.345 *Cochino*	4/1945	Foundered off Norway 1949
SS.346 *Corporal*	6/1945	Turkish *Ikinci Inonu* 1973
SS.347 *Cubera*	6/1945	Venezuelan *Tiburay* 1972
SS.348 *Cusk*	7/1945	Stricken 1969
SS.349 *Diodan*	9/1945	Sold 1972 for scrapping
SS.350 *Dogfish*	10/1945	Brazilian *Guanabara* 1972
SS.351 *Greenfish* (ex-*Doncella*)	12/1945	Brazilian *Amazonas* 1973
SS.352 *Halfbeak* (ex-*Dory*)	2/1946	Stricken 1971
SS.361 *Golet*	8/1943	War loss Jun 1944
SS.362 *Guavina*	8/1943	Sunk as target 1967
SS.363 *Guitarro*	9/1943	Turkish *Preveze* 1954
SS.364 *Hammerhead*	10/1943	Turkish *Cerbe* 1954
SS.365 *Hardhead*	12/1943	Greek *Papanikolis* 1972
SS.366 *Hawkbill*	1/1944	*Zeeleeuw* 1954
SS.367 *Icefish*	2/1944	Netherlands *Walrus* 1953
SS.368 *Jallao*	3/1944	Stricken 1974
SS.369 *Kete*	4/1944	War loss Mar 1945
SS.370 *Kraken*	4/1944	Spanish *Almirante Garcia de los Reyes*

Hull no and name	launched	fate
SS.371 *Lagarto*	5/1944	War loss May 1945
SS.372 *Lamprey*	6/1944	Argentine *Santa Fe* 1960
SS.373 *Lizardfish*	7/1944	Italian *Evangelista Torricelli* 1960
SS.374 *Loggerhead*	8/1944	Sold 1969 for scrapping
SS.375 *Macabi*	9/1944	Argentine *Santiago del Estero* 1960
SS.376 *Mapiro*	11/1944	Turkish *Piri Reis* 1960
SS.377 *Menhaden*	12/1944	Striken 1973
SS.378 *Mero*	1/1945	Turkish *Hizir Reis* 1960

USS *Sea Devil* (SS.400) on completion of a refit at Mare Island in mid-March 1946, looking forward (below) and aft (right). The ringed areas indicate equipment modified or added during the refit. A second 5-in/25-cal gun has been added forward of the conning tower and the sonar transducer on the forward casing is ringed (right), as are the hydroplane guards on the stern

Hull no and name	launched	fate
SS.381 *Sandlance* (ex-*Ojanca*, ex-*Orca*)	6/1943	Brazilian *Rio Grande do Sul* 1963
SS.382 *Picuda* (ex-*Obispo*)	7/1943	Spanish *Narciso Monturiol* 1972
SS.383 *Pampanito*	7/1943	Stricken 1971
SS.384 *Parche*	7/1943	Sold 1970 for scrapping
SS.385 *Bang*	8/1943	Spanish *Cosme Garcia* 1972
SS.386 *Pilotfish*	8/1943	Sunk as target 1948
SS.387 *Pintado*	9/1943	Sold 1969 for scrapping
SS.388 *Pipefish*	10/1943	Sold 1969 for scrapping
SS.389 *Piranha*	10/1943	Sold 1970 for scrapping
SS.390 *Plaice*	11/1943	Brazilian *Bahia* 1963
SS.391 *Pomfret*	10/1943	Turkish *Oruc Reis* 1971
SS.392 *Sterlet* (ex-*Pudiano*)	10/1943	Sunk as target 1969
SS.393 *Queenfish*	11/1943	Sunk as target 1963
SS.394 *Razorback*	1/1944	Turkish *Murat Reis* 1970
SS.395 *Redfish*	1/1944	Sunk as target 1969
SS.396 *Ronquil*	1/1944	Spanish *Isaac Peral* 1971
SS.397 *Scabbardfish*	1/1944	Greek *Traina* 1964
SS.398 *Segundo*	2/1944	Stricken 1970

Hull no and name	launched	fate
SS.399 *Sea Cat*	2/1944	Sunk as target 1968
SS.400 *Sea Devil*	2/1944	Sunk as target 1965
SS.401 *Sea Dog*	3/1944	Stricken 1968 for trials
SS.402 *Sea Fox*	3/1944	Turkish *Burak Reis* 1970
SS.403 *Atule*	3/1944	Stricken 1974
SS.404 *Spikefish*	4/1944	Sunk as target 1963
SS.405 *Sea Owl*	5/1944	Sold 1971 for scrapping
SS.406 *Sea Poacher*	5/1944	Stricken 1973
SS.407 *Sea Robin*	5/1944	Sold 1971 for scrapping
SS.408 *Sennet*	6/1944	Stricken 1968
SS.409 *Piper* (ex-*Awa*)	6/1944	Stricken 1970
SS.410 *Threadfin*	6/1944	Turkish *Birina Inonu* 1973
SS.411 *Spadefish*	1/1943	Sold 1969 for scrapping
SS.412 *Trepang*	3/1944	Sunk as target 1969
SS.413 *Spot*	5/1944	Chilean *Al Simpson* 1962
SS.414 *Springer*	8/1944	Chilean *Captain Thomson* 1961
SS.415 *Stickleback*	1/1945	Sunk in collision 1958
SS.416 *Tiru*	9/1947	Ran aground 1966 but refloated and stricken

USS *Guitarro* (SS.363) at Mare Island, June 1954, looking aft. Her conning tower has been streamlined and the light AA guns removed

US Navy

US Navy

US Navy

USS *Cusk* (SS.348) in late September 1947, being equipped for launching the Loon guided missiles (above left), and under way (above right). Tracking radar has been fitted to the conning tower, while the cylindrical hangar with hemispherical door and launching ramp are positioned aft. *Below:* USS *Carbonero* (SS.337) launches a Republic JB-2 Loon copy of the German V-1 flying bomb during Exercise Miki, November 1949. JATO (jet-assisted takeoff) bottles were used to launch the missile and to give it sufficient speed for the pulse-jet to be able to function

Richard P Hallion Collection

Baleares

Baleares

Spanish heavy cruiser class. On May 31, 1928, the Spanish navy ordered two heavy cruisers to be named *Baleares* and *Canarias* from the Ferrol dockyard of La Sociedal Española de Construcción Naval. The design had been prepared by Sir Philip Watts, who had been Director of Naval Construction for the (British) Royal Navy from 1902 to 1912. Their design was closely based on the latest British heavy cruisers, the *County* Class, the first of which had been laid down in 1924.

The Washington Treaty of 1922 laid down that new heavy cruisers built by signatory nations should not carry guns larger than 8-in calibre, nor should they have a standard displacement greater than 10000 tons. The *County*s were the first British cruisers built under these limitations. They incorporated a new twin 8-in power-operated turret, with a very high rate of fire, and an unusually high maximum elevation to enable them to be used for antiaircraft fire. They had a very high freeboard to ensure adequate seaworthiness and a long range—16740 km (10400 miles) at 11 knots—for worldwide operations.

Although the *Baleares* and her sister were very similar to the *County*s, they were not identical. The most obvious difference was in the superstructure and funnels. The *County*s had three funnels, and a fairly small bridge. Watts' original design for the Spanish cruisers had two funnels. However, the Spanish changed their mind, and the ships were completed with the uptakes trunked into one enormous funnel. *Baleares* and *Canarias* were fitted with large tower bridges.

The Spanish needed high speed rather than long range, and their engines developed an extra 10000 shp giving 1.5 knots higher speed, but the oil fuel was reduced from 3400 tons to 2794 tons, giving a maximum range of 12550 km (7800 miles) at 11 knots. The *County*s' armour gave (in theory) protection against 8-in shells, whereas the two Spanish ships were only partially protected against 6-in shells, reflecting the different requirements of the two navies. The 8-in mountings on the *Baleares* and *Canarias* were given 70° elevation. *Baleares* could be distinguished from her sister by the absence of a lip to her funnel, which *Canarias* possessed.

Baleares was launched on April 20, 1932, but her construction was delayed by the changes in design, and she was not quite complete when the Spanish Civil War broke out in 1936. It is ironic that the Spanish were to rebuild *Canarias* to the original design in 1950-51.

Ferrol was originally held by the Government (Republicans), but was soon captured by the Nationalists, who hastily completed the two heavy cruisers. Most of the navy was in Republican hands, and they were badly needed to redress the balance. Even so, *Baleares* did not receive her main armament until the summer of 1937. However, she had already taken part in operations. In February 1937 she bombarded the Republican enclave of Malaga on the southeast coast, with *Canarias* and the destroyer *Velasco*.

Both heavy cruisers were extensively used for convoy work, and early on March 6, 1938 they were escorting a convoy from Sicily when they encountered a Republican force of two cruisers and four destroyers off Cape

The Italian submarine *Balilla* was laid down for Germany but requisitioned by Italy in 1915

Palos, near Cartagena, steaming on an opposite course. Both sides were taken by surprise, and in a confused action the Republican destroyer *Lepanto* hit *Baleares* with one torpedo amidships. There was a heavy explosion and she sank almost immediately. 470 survivors were picked up by the British destroyers *Boreas* and *Kempenfelt*, which were part of the Nyons Neutrality patrol.

Displacement: 10000 tons (standard), 13200 tons (full load) *Length:* 194 m (636 ft 6 in) *Beam:* 19.5 m (64 ft 0 in) *Draught:* 6.5 m (21 ft 4 in) *Machinery:* 4-shaft geared steam turbines, 90000 shp=33 knots *Protection:* 38 mm-51 mm (1½-2 in) sides; 105 mm (4 in) magazines; 25 mm (1 in) turrets *Armament:* 8 8-in (203-mm); 8 4.7-in (120-mm); 4 1.5-in (38-mm); 12 21-in (53-cm) torpedo tubes (4 triple mountings) *Crew:* 800

Balilla

Italian submarine. In the years before the First World War, when submarine technology was changing rapidly, navies tended to order prototypes from other countries' shipyards for comparison. Just as the Italians ordered a U-Boat from Krupps, the German navy ordered a submarine from Fiat-San Giorgio in 1913. She was laid down at La Spezia in August 1913, as *U 42*, but was still under construction when Italy entered the First World War against Austria-Hungary in June 1915. She was named *Balilla* and launched on August 4, 1915.

The *Balilla* was a single-hulled boat designed to dive to a depth of 50 m. She resembled the contemporary *Pacinotti* Class in dimensions, characteristics and machinery, but had four torpedo tubes instead of five (two forward and two aft). An unusual feature was the raised casing forward, presumably to improve seakeeping in the North Sea, for Mediterranean submarines were notoriously ill-suited to the rougher conditions encountered in the North Sea.

The machinery was twin screw diesel/electric, with two 1300-bhp Fiat diesel motors and two 450-hp Savigliano electric motors. In service the diesels were limited to 800-bhp each for safety, giving a surface speed of 10 knots. It is not clear if her gun armament was part of the original German specification or an Italian modification after she was taken over. In any case it marks the first installation of antiaircraft guns in a submarine.

The *Balilla* was completed on August 8, 1915 and after trials was sent to Brindisi to join the 8th Squadron in February 1916. This flotilla of submarines was employed on coast

defence against the frequent raids by Austro-Hungarian forces. On the night of July 14, 1916 the *Balilla* was caught charging her batteries north west of the island of Lissa by the Austrian torpedo boats *65F* and *66F*. She was sunk with all hands but after putting up an heroic but hopeless fight.

Displacement: 728/825 tonnes (surfaced/submerged) *Length:* 65 m (213 ft 3 in) oa *Beam:* 6.05 m (19 ft 8½ in) *Draught:* 4.17 m (13 ft 8 in) *Machinery:* (surfaced) 2-shaft diesels, 2600 bhp=14 knots; (submerged) electric motors, 900 hp=9 knots *Armament:* 2 3-in (76-mm)/30-cal AA; 4 45-cm (17.7-in) torpedo tubes (6 torpedoes carried) *Crew:* 38

Balilla

Italian submarine class. In 1924 the Italian navy asked Ansaldo-San Giorgio to design a cruiser-submarine with high endurance, good surface speed and powerful armament. Four submarines were built to the design which resulted, all at the Muggiano (La Spezia) yard of Odero-Terni. By embarking on the construction of oceangoing submarines the Italian navy hoped to extend its operations outside the Mediterranean. The new African colonies provided bases from which submarines could attack shipping in the Red Sea and the Indian Ocean.

The *Balilla* design was double-hulled and differed from most others in having a 425-hp Fiat Q 304 Type generator to provide auxiliary power and to charge the batteries. The Italians never went to the extremes of heavy gun-armament found in other navies' cruiser-submarines, and were content with a single 120-mm gun in this instance. It was originally mounted in a revolving turret forward of the conning tower. In 1934 a new type of longer 120-mm gun was substituted and the turret was removed. As in other Italian submarines the conning tower was very large.

As originally designed the class was to have a stern launching-tube for four mines, but this was only fitted in the *Antonio Sciesa*.

The *Enrico Toti* caught the British submarine *Rainbow* on the surface in the Gulf of Taranto on October 15, 1940 and sank her. However, as a class they were too big and unwieldy for operations in the Mediterranean, and neither were they suitable for operations in the Atlantic. The *Domenico Millelire* and *Balilla* were laid up in April 1941 and used as the floating oil storage tanks *GR.248* and *GR.247* respectively. The *Antonio Sciesa* and the *Enrico Toti* were used as transports to carry vital material to

Name	laid down	launched	completed
Balilla	1/1925	2/1927	7/1928
Domenico Millelire	1/1925	9/1927	8/1928
Antonio Sciesa	10/1925	8/1928	4/1929
Enrico Toti	1/1925	4/1928	9/1928

The Ballester Molina, or HAFDASA, .45-in automatic, virtually a copy of the Colt M1911

North Africa, but on September 6, 1942 the *Sciesa* was damaged at Tobruk by American aircraft. She was run aground to stop her from sinking, but proved to be beyond repair and was scuttled on November 12, when the port was captured by the 8th Army. The *Enrico Toti* was laid up on May 1, 1943, and with her two sisters was later scrapped.

Displacement: 1450/1904 tons (surfaced/submerged) *Length:* 86.75 m (284 ft 7 in) oa *Beam:* 7.8 m (25 ft 7 in) *Draught:* 4.7 m (15 ft 5 in) *Machinery:* (surfaced) 2-shaft diesels, 4900-bhp+425-bhp auxiliary=17½ knots (16 knots actual); (submerged) 2 electric motors, 2200 hp=8.9 knots (7 knots actual) *Armament:* 1 120-mm (4.7-in)/27-cal (replaced by 1 120-mm/45-cal in 1934); 4 13.2-mm machine-guns; 6 53-cm (21-in) torpedo tubes (four forward, two aft, 16 torpedoes carried); 4 mines (*Antonio Sciesa* only) *Crew:* 77 (approx)

Balilla, Ansaldo A-1

Italian single-seat fighter. One of the fastest combat aircraft of the First World War, this trim fighting scout was a source of pride to the Italians for it marked a release from total dependence on foreign designs in this class of aircraft.

The A-1 was designed by Ing G Brezzi of the Società Gio Ansaldo, but was strongly influenced by the Savoia/Verduzio S.V. scout flown in March 1917. Design proceeded during the summer of that year and the first A-1 (often written A.1) was ready in late September. The first Italian fighter was remarkably small, but had 220 hp available from an SPA 6A six-cylinder water-cooled engine, which was fully cowled. The biplane wings had equal area and no stagger, and the upper centre-section was cut away to improve pilot view. Two Vickers 7.7-mm machine-guns were mounted in the top decking, synchronized to fire past the propeller.

On test the new fighter proved to be faster than any known fighter then in use, but when the three leading Italian fighter pilots (Francesco Baracca, Piccio and Ruffo di Calabria) evaluated the A-1 in November 1917 they criticized its poor manoeuvrability. For this reason production was on a limited scale, the number built for the Corpo Aeronautica Militare (Italian Air Force) being only 108 (some reports claim 150). Most of these were issued to home defence units, and only a dozen or two were issued to front-line squadrons, where the type was officially named Balilla (Hunter).

After the Armistice 75 Balillas were supplied to the newly formed Polish air force, and the first 20 reached the Russo-Polish front at a crucial time in June 1920, some at once going into action with the Kościuszko Squadron. After the war, in 1921, the other

55 aircraft arrived, and confronted what was by then the Soviet Union. These were supplemented by 50 more built under licence by Plage & Laśkiewicz at Lublin. Ansaldo supplied a further batch to Lithuania, while some Italian Balillas were used as aerobatic display machines.

Span: 7.68 m (25 ft 2½ in) *Length:* 6.76 m (22 ft 5 in) *Gross weight:* 885 kg (1951 lb) *Maximum speed:* 225 km/h (140 mph)

Ballester Molina

Argentine automatic pistol. The Ballester Molina automatic pistol was made before and during the Second World War by the Argentine company Hispano-Argentino Fabrica de Automobiles SA, from which comes its alternative name, the HAFDASA. It is virtually a copy of the Colt .45 M1911 pistol, the only difference being in the trigger linkage and the absence of a grip safety. It is about half an inch longer than the Colt, though the butt is slightly smaller and seems to fit better in a small hand. The method of operation is the same, using the Browning 'swinging link' system of locking barrel and breech together. The finish is not comparable with that of the Colt, but it is a serviceable and reliable weapon. It is more common in Europe than might be expected, since numbers were bought by an Allied purchasing commission during the war for supply to SOE and other clandestine agencies operating resistance against German forces in the occupied countries of Europe.

Length: 229 mm (9.0 in) *Weight:* 1.134 kg (2 lb 8 oz) *Barrel:* 127 mm (5.0 in) *Magazine:* 8 rounds *Calibre:* .45 Auto Colt

Baltimore

US protected cruiser. In August 1886 the Congress of the United States authorized a protected cruiser, the second to be built for the USN. Because of the lack of experience in building steel cruisers the Navy Department was authorized to approach a foreign builder, and as with the previous cruiser, USS *Charleston*, the firm chosen was Sir W G Armstrong, Mitchell & Co of Newcastle-upon-Tyne. The contract was only to be for the design and plans as the construction was to be in an American yard.

The keel of Cruiser No 3 was laid in 1886 at the Philadelphia yard of William Cramp & Sons. Christened *Baltimore*, she was launched on October 6, 1888 and commissioned on January 7, 1890. She was similar to other Elswick designs but had a much heavier armament, with two 8-in guns side by side on the forecastle and the poop, and three 6-in

The protected cruiser USS *Baltimore*, designed for the United States Navy by Armstrongs

US Navy

Baltimore

guns on either side amidships. She resembled the famous *Esmeralda* built for Chile in 1884, but was larger to allow for a heavier scale of protection and armament. Another improvement in the American ship was the raised forecastle, which improved seakeeping.

In May 1890 the *Baltimore* became the flagship of the North Atlantic Squadron but transferred to the South Pacific Station in 1891. She was at Hong Kong when the war against Spain broke out, but sailed with Commodore Dewey's squadron from Mirs Bay on April 27, 1898. Dewey's ships arrived in Manila Bay on May 1 and destroyed the Spanish squadron with virtually no loss

In May 1907 the ship was put into reserve at Charleston navy yard, where she served as a receiving ship until September 1912. In 1913-14 she underwent conversion to a minelayer and spent the next two years carrying out experimental minelaying in Chesapeake Bay and along the Atlantic coast. As United States involvement in the First World War became more likely she switched to training duties, but the need for extensive mining in the European theatre led to her being sent across the Atlantic in 1918. She arrived at the Clyde on March 8 and between April 13 and May 2 laid 900 mines in the North Channel off the north coast of Ireland. In June she joined the 1st Mine Squadron (USN) at Inverness to work on laying the Northern Barrage between the Orkneys and Norway. As soon as this was over she sailed on September 28 for the USA, where she returned to the task of laying experimental mines near the Virgin Islands.

After a brief spell in the Pacific Fleet, during which she changed her designation to *CM.1* she was taken out of commission at Pearl Harbor in September 1922. She lay as a hulk there until she was sold for scrapping in February 1942.

Displacement: 4600 tons (normal) *Length:* 102.11 m (335 ft) oa *Beam:* 14.78 m (48 ft 6 in) *Draught:* 6.25 m (20 ft 6 in) mean *Machinery:* 2-shaft horizontal triple-expansion, 10 000 ihp=19½ knots *Protection:* 64 mm-102 mm (2½-4 in) deck *Armament:* (As built) 4 8-in (203-mm)/35-cal (4×1); 6 6-in (152-mm)/30-cal (6×1); 4 6-pdr (57-mm) (4×1); 2 3-pdr (47-mm) (2×1); 6 1-pdr (37-mm); 5 14-in (35.5-cm) torpedo tubes (above water); (From 1901) 12 6-in/40-cal (12×1); 4 6-pdr (4×1); (From 1915) 4 6-in; 4 6-pdr; 180 mines; (From 1917) 4 5-in (127-mm) (4×1); 2 3-in (76-mm) AA (2×1); 4 6-pdr *Crew:* 386 (320 as minelayer)

Baltimore

US heavy cruiser class. On July 1, 1940 under the Two-Ocean Navy programme, the US Navy ordered four heavy (8-in gunned) cruisers as the first installment of a massive rebuilding of American naval strength. The new class was to be called the *Baltimore* Class and as the Washington Treaty limits had now lapsed the Bureau of Ships was able to build to what it considered the right displacement, ie 13 600 tons as opposed to 10 000. In fact the US Navy was only doing what the Japanese, German and Italian navies had already decided to do in secret, which is an interesting example of how different navies ultimately come to the same conclusions about optimum size.

US Navy

USS *Baltimore* (CA.68) with two Vought OS2U-3 Kingfisher floatplanes on the catapult

The design followed closely the previous *Wichita* (1937) but copied the layout of the contemporary *Cleveland* Class light cruisers. They were extremely powerful-looking ships with high freeboard, two tall capped funnels and superstructure divided into two distinct blocks. With a beamy hull there was ample room for a heavy antiaircraft armament of 12 5-in guns, disposed hexagonally in twin turrets, and six quad 40-mm Bofors mountings

USS *Baltimore* off Boston, Mass, in September 1943. Heavily armed and having a large radius of action, the heavy cruisers of this class were, at the time of their completion, probably the finest of their type in the world

Hull No and name	laid down	launched	completed
CA.68 **Baltimore**	5/1941	7/1942	4/1943
CA.69 **Boston**	6/1941	8/1942	6/1943
CA.70 **Canberra** (ex-*Pittsburgh*)	9/1941	4/1943	10/1943
CA.71 **Quincy** (ex-*St Paul*)	10/1941	6/1943	12/1943
CA.72 **Pittsburgh** (ex-*Albany*)	2/1943	2/1944	10/1944
CA.73 **Saint Paul** (ex-*Rochester*)	2/1943	9/1944	2/1945
CA.74 **Columbus**	6/1943	11/1944	6/1945
CA.75 **Helena** (ex-*Des Moines*)	9/1943	4/1945	9/1945
CA.122 **Oregon City**	4/1944	6/1945	—
CA.123 **Albany**	3/1944	6/1945	—
CA.124 **Rochester**	5/1944	8/1945	—
CA.125 **Northampton**	8/1944	—	—
CA.130 **Bremerton**	2/1943	7/1944	4/1945
CA.131 **Fall River**	4/1943	8/1944	7/1945
CA.132 **Macon**	6/1943	10/1944	8/1945
CA.133 **Toledo**	9/1943	5/1945	10/1946
CA.134 **Los Angeles**	7/1943	8/1944	7/1945
CA.135 **Chicago**	7/1943	8/1944	1/1945

US Navy

amidships. The protection was heavy by cruiser standards, a 6-in belt extending between the turrets, and a 2-3-in deck. All living and working spaces were given air-conditioning, and as a result no side scuttles were provided. The great size also meant a big radius of action, important in a class intended for action in the Pacific.

The first group was quickly followed by an order for a further four placed on September 9, 1940, but the emphasis on other ship types led to a two-year gap. A further ten were ordered on August 7, 1942 but only six were completed by 1945; three were completed to a modified design (the *Oregon City* Class) and one was suspended for many years, and finally completed as a command ship. Because of steel shortages, and the urgent need for destroyers and escorts, work on the class was not pushed forward with as much urgency as might be expected, and the lead ship did not commission until April 15, 1943. CA.68-75 and CA.122-125 were built by Bethlehem Steel at Quincy, Massachusetts, and CA.130-135 by New York Shipbuilding at Camden.

Several were renamed to commemorate older cruisers sunk in the fighting around Guadalcanal, but in a quixotic gesture the *Pittsburgh* was renamed *Canberra* in honour of the Australian 'County' Class heavy cruiser sunk at Savo Island. This proved embarrassing to the Australians, for there was an inter-allied agreement not to duplicate major ships' names: as a result of the American decision the Australians could not bestow the name on their own replacement for their *Canberra*. The antiaircraft armament was increased before completion, and the first ships carried 48 Bofors guns, two extra quads on either side forward, one on the forecastle, two aft and one at the stern. In the later ships the guns on the stern were changed to two twin mounts because the massive aircraft cranes tended to mask the arcs of fire of one mount set to port. The total of 20-mm guns varied from 22 to 24, and late in the war some of the singles were exchanged for manually operated twins.

One unfortunate feature was retained from the pre-war *Brooklyn* Class cruisers, the large hangar for floatplanes under the quarterdeck. In theory this could be used to house up to four OS2U-3 Kingfisher floatplanes and allow maintenance to be carried out under cover. The position proved to be a bad one, for the large resonant cavity above the propellers caused vibration and there was always a risk of the hatch being damaged in heavy weather. As a result only two aircraft were carried, on the catapults.

The class performed very well in action and were involved in all the campaigns which took the US Navy across the Pacific, from the Gilbert Islands to Iwo Jima. *Canberra* was badly damaged by a torpedo off Formosa in October 1944, and on June 5, 1945 the *Pittsburgh* lost her bow in a typhoon. This caused some misgivings about the standards of wartime shipbuilding, especially as she held the record for the class, being built in only 20 months. The *Quincy* was at Normandy in June 1944, the only one of the class to see service in Europe. Several ships served with distinction in the Korean war as well, but they were somewhat out of date by the mid-1950s, as well as being expensive to run, with large crews.

Los Angeles, Helena, Macon and *Toledo* were converted to carry the Regulus surface-to-surface missile in the same period, but this involved merely siting a ramp on the stern in similar fashion to the now-discarded catapults. Another change which affected all the ships in commission was the stripping of all 20-mm AA guns and the replacement of quadruple 40-mm guns by the new twin 3-in/50-cal rapid-fire mounting. The after pair of gun 'buckets' were not used in peacetime, and so only ten 3-in mountings were installed.

In 1952 the *Boston* and *Canberra* were taken in hand by the New York Shipbuilding Corporation (the same firm which had built many of their sisters) for conversion to the world's first guided-missile-armed cruisers. The after 8-in turret, weighing 143 tons, was removed, along with the aftermost 5-in twin AA gun. The entire superstructure abaft the bridge was rebuilt, with a lattice foremast, a single funnel and two sets of twin launchers and directors for the Terrier RIM-2 beam-riding missile. The two ships recommissioned as CAG.1 and CAG.2 in November 1955 and June 1956 respectively.

A much more ambitious conversion was given to the *Chicago* and *Columbus*, involving complete rebuilding of the topsides which permitted a 'double-ended' missile armament. They and the former *Oregon City* Class

Baltimore Martin

Albany formed a new class when they commissioned in 1962-64, and are described under a separate heading (referred to below).

The *Macon* was stricken in 1969, *Baltimore* and *Fall River* in 1971, *Pittsburgh, Quincy* and *Bremerton* in 1973, and *Helena, Toledo* and *Los Angeles* in 1974. The *St Paul* was modified to serve as the flagship of the 7th Fleet in the Western Pacific, and was the last all-gun cruiser to be in commission. She was decommissioned in 1971 but was still on the Navy List in 1976.

See also *Albany* Class, *Northampton, Oregon City* Class, Terrier RIM-2.

Displacement: 13 600 tons (standard), 17 070 tons (full load) *Length:* (CA.68-71) 205.3 m (673 ft 6 in) oa; (CA.72 ff) 205.74 m (675 ft) oa *Beam:* 21.56 m (70 ft 9 in) *Draught:* 6.25 m (20 ft 6 in) normal, 7.92 m (26 ft) max *Machinery:* 4-shaft geared steam turbines, 120 000 shp=33 knots *Protection:* 152 mm (6 in) belt; 50-76 mm (2-3 in) deck; 76-152 mm (3-6 in) turrets; 203 mm (8 in) conning tower *Armament:* (As built) 9 8-in (203-mm)/55-cal (3×3); 12 5-in (127-mm)/38-cal DP (6×2); 48 40-mm AA (11×4, 2×2 or 12×4); 22-28 single 20-mm AA; (After 1945) 9 8-in; 12 5-in DP; 20 3-in AA *Crew:* 1142 (peace), 1700 (war)

(*Boston* and *Canberra* as CAG.1 and CAG.2) *Displacement:* 13 300 tons (standard), 17 500 tons (full load) *Dimensions, Machinery* and *Protection:* Unchanged *Armament:* 6 8-in/55-cal (2×3); 10 5-in/38-cal DP (5×2); 8 3-in/50-cal Mk 33 (4×2); 2 twin Terrier *Crew:* 1273

Baltimore Martin

American medium bomber. Though it received the US Army Air Corps designation of A-30, the Baltimore was one of the few combat-worthy American machines of the Second World War that was never used by any of the US forces. The original design, the Martin 187, was produced to meet a British Air Ministry order of May 1940 for a further batch of Martin 167 Maryland light attack bombers (such as had been in quantity production for France) with deeper fuselages to overcome the Maryland's drawback of preventing any crew-member from reaching any other in flight. The British also requested 96 kg (211 lb) of armour and self-sealing fuel tanks, as well as many smaller modifications

that combat had shown to be desirable.

After the fall of France, Martin realized that instant delivery would make little difference to the war and that they had a major redesign job on their hands. To handle the increased weight they changed from the Twin Wasp engine to a pair of 1600 hp Wright R-2600 Cyclone 14-cylinder radials, and when the supposed new mark of Maryland flew in June 1941 it was given the name of Baltimore.

The first 400 aircraft, ordered on British account in May 1940, were delivered in three marks: the Baltimore I, with a manually aimed .303-in (7.7-mm) Vickers K in the dorsal position; the Mk II, with two such guns in this position; and the Mk III, with a Boulton Paul turret (shipped from England) with two or four 0.303-in Brownings. Production then continued with further batches under lend-lease contracts, for which purpose the Baltimore received the US designation A-30.

After delivering 281 Mk IIIAs, similar to

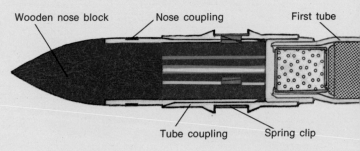

Assembly of the two filled sections of the British Army Bangalore Torpedo 1½-in Mk 2. The forward section is fitted with a hard-wood nosecap, the rear with the igniter

Wooden nose block   Nose coupling   First tube

Tube coupling   Spring clip

the III but on lend-lease account, Martin produced 294 Mk IV with a Martin twin .5-in (12.7-mm) dorsal turret, completing the programme of 1575 aircraft with 600 Mk V with 1700-hp R-2600 engines. All models had two 0.303-in Vickers K or Browning guns in the rear ventral position, and most had four fixed 0.303-in Brownings in the outer wings firing ahead; a few had various batteries of four or six guns firing obliquely down or to the rear. Bombload, all internal, was up to 907 kg (2000 lb).

Almost all Baltimores served in North Africa, the Mediterranean and Italy, on bombing and close-support missions, often at

low level. Users were the RAF, South African Air Force, Royal Navy and, after November 1943, the co-belligerent Italian air force, whose Stormo Baltimore was the chief Italian unit of offensive air power over Yugoslavia and the Balkans. Though quite fast and popular with its crews, the Baltimore was already obsolescent when the last was delivered in May 1944, and after VE Day it was quickly withdrawn from service.

Span: 18.69 m (61 ft 4 in) *Length:* 14.78 m (48 ft 6 in) *Gross weight:* (Mk I) 10 413 kg (22 958 lb), (Mk V) 12 632 kg (27 850 lb) *Maximum speed:* (typical of all) 496 km/h (308 mph)

Bandeirante EMBRAER

Brazilian transport and multirole utility aircraft. Designed in Brazil under the leadership of Max Holste, the former French constructor, the Bandeirante (Pioneer) has been developed in many forms and in all of these has shown itself to be a most capable aircraft.

The YC-95 prototype was planned as a simple unpressurized twin-turboprop transport for liaison, casualty evacuation and crew training. It flew on October 26, 1968, powered by two 680-hp Pratt & Whitney Canada PT6A-27 engines. In 1972 this model went into production as the EMB-110, with deliveries beginning in February 1973. A total of 60 were built for the Brazilian air force, most of them 12-seat C-95 transports, plus three for the Chilean navy.

By 1977 more than 160 Bandeirantes had been sold to military, para-military and civilian customers, and the following military

Martin Baltimore Mk III with Boulton Paul dorsal turret and four Browning machine-guns below the fuselage firing obliquely to the rear

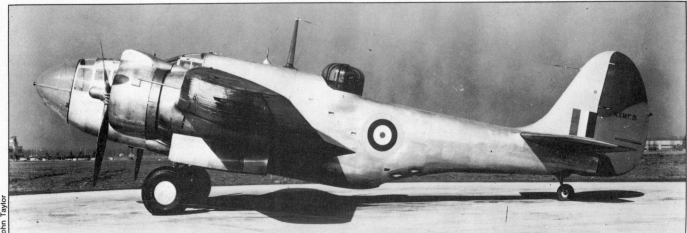

Name	laid down	launched	completed	builder
Fratelli Bandiera	2/1938	8/1929	9/1930	Cantieri Navali Triestini, Monfalcone
Luciano Manara	2/1928	10/1929	6/1930	Triestini, Monfalcone
Ciro Menotti	5/1928	12/1929	8/1930	Odero-Terni-Orlando, Muggiano (La Spezia)
Santorre Santarosa	5/1928	10/1929	7/1930	Muggiano (La Spezia)

versions had been flown or developed:
EMB-110A. Variant equipped for calibrating navaids and ILS installations; first two ordered by the Brazilian air force and other customers.
EMB-110F. All-cargo version.
EMB-110K. Similar to the new 15-seat civil model but with freight floor and large freight door; built for the Brazilian air force.

The EMB-111 was a major redesign to

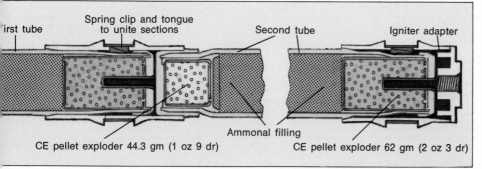

CE pellet exploder 44.3 gm (1 oz 9 dr)   Ammonal filling   CE pellet exploder 62 gm (2 oz 3 dr)

produce a maritime patrol aircraft for Commando Costeiro, the Brazilian air force coastal command. It was powered by two 750-hp PT6A-34 engines and had increased fuel capacity and gross weight. It carried AIL APS-128 search radar in bulged nose, Litton LN-33 inertial navigation system and extensive avionics and mission equipment including flares, smoke grenades, searchlight and eight 5-in (127-mm) rockets. The first flight of the EMB-111 was scheduled for July 1977.

The following data are typical of previous (transport) versions.

Span: 15.32 m (50 ft 3 in) *Length:* 14.23 m (46 ft 8¼ in) *Gross weight:* 5600 kg (12 345 lb) *Maximum speed:* 434 km/h (270 mph)

Bandiera

Italian submarine class. In 1927 General Curio Bernardis designed an improved version of the *Pisani* Class. The hull form of the *Pisani* was retained but an increase in overall dimensions allowed the installation of more powerful machinery. The greater space aft allowed for an extra pair of torpedo tubes, and with more fuel the class had 805 km (500 miles) more endurance on the surface.

Experience with the *Pisani* Class had shown that the hull lacked stability, and so it was decided to fit 'bulges' in the form of additional saddle-tanks. This modification was incorporated in the boats after completion, and as a result the trials surface speed of about 17½ knots was cut to 15 in service. They were still unsatisfactory, however, for the same reasons that had led to strong criticism

of the *Pisani* Class. The bow tended to bury itself and seakeeping was generally poor. To cure this the four boats were taken in hand for a second reconstruction, to fit a large quick-blowing tank in the bow to reduce pitching. At the same time the conning tower was enlarged and given an enclosed steering position.

The four boats were formed into a flotilla based on Taranto from 1931, but in 1933 they were sent to Brindisi and the following year to Naples. Although sent to North Africa in 1935, all except the *Bandiera*, which went on to the Red Sea, returned home at the time of the Spanish Civil War. The *Manara*, *Menotti* and *Santarosa* covertly supported the Nationalist cause, and carried out four war patrols in Spanish waters in 1937-38, though without any notable successes.

By 1941 the four boats were being used as transports to take supplies to Tripoli and Bardia. In 1942 the *Bandiera*, *Menotti* and *Manara* were assigned to training but the *Santarosa* continued as a supply submarine. On June 20, 1943, after running aground off Tripoli she was torpedoed by the British *MTB 260* and eventually had to be scuttled. The remaining boats were surrendered in 1943 and interned at Malta. After lying in various Mediterranean ports they were returned to Italy, and officially stricken on February 1, 1948 to comply with the terms of the Peace Treaty; they were subsequently sold for scrapping.

Displacement: 933-941/1096-1153 tons (surfaced/submerged) *Length:* 69.8 m (229 ft 0 in) oa *Beam:* 7.21/7.3 m (23 ft 8 in/23 ft 11 in) (as built/as modified) *Draught:* 5.18/5.26 m (17 ft 0 in/17 ft 3 in) (as built/as modified) *Machinery:* 2-shaft diesel/electric, 3000 bhp/1300 shp= 15.1/8.2 knots (surfaced/submerged) *Armament:* 1 102-mm (4-in)/35-cal; 2 13.2-mm machine-guns; 8 53-cm (21-in) torpedo tubes (four forward, four aft, 12 torpedoes carried); (*Menotti* from 1942) 1 100-mm (3.9-in)/47 cal *Endurance:* 4740 miles at 8½ knots/60 miles at 4 knots (surfaced/submerged) *Crew:* 52

Bangalore Torpedo

Universal wire-cutting device. The Bangalore Torpedo consisted of a 1.8-m (6-ft) light steel tube of 38-mm (1½-in) diameter, packed with 1.8 kg (4 lb) of ammonal blasting explosive. The ends of the charge were prepared for detonators, while the tube had 'male' and 'female' bayonet joints at its ends, with spring locking clips, so that a number of tubes could be locked together. A conical hardwood head went into the front end of a set of tubes, while an electric detonator was fitted into the rear. This assembly—of as many tubes as required—could then be pushed along the ground and under a barbed wire entanglement, the smooth nose allowing it to slide through without snagging. Once in position, the electric detonator was fired and the entire 'torpedo' then detonated, blowing a gap through the entanglement.

The torpedo took its name from being invented at Bangalore, India, in 1912 by a Captain McClintock of the Indian Sappers and Miners. The Russo-Japanese war, and to a lesser extent the South African war, had introduced barbed wire to the battlefield and trials were carried out at Bangalore to determine the best method of overcoming this new problem. McClintock's torpedo was originally a 5.5-m (18-ft) length of water piping stuffed with 27.2 kg (60 lb) of dynamite which, according to legend, not only demolished the barbed wire by its blast but almost demolished the spectators as well. Suitably redesigned, the Bangalore Torpedo was widely used during the First World War and was adopted in principle by several other nations, but due to the changing style of warfare it saw less use in the Second World War and is now virtually obsolete.

Bang-Gevaer

Danish automatic rifle series. Soren H Bang, a Danish designer, was responsible for a series of semi-automatic rifles which were extensively tested over a long period of time but which never quite lived up to their promise.

Bang's first patent was taken out in 1901, for a rifle with a sleeve or cup surrounding the muzzle. This was connected, via an operating rod running back beneath the barrel, to the bolt. When the rifle was fired, the rush of gas following the bullet pushed the sleeve forward and, through the medium of the operating rod, opened the bolt to extract the empty case; a return spring then returned the bolt and chambered the next round.

Several experimental models were made and tests were carried out in a number of countries. The US Ordnance Department tested one in 1911 and reported quite favourably on it, but its complexity and expense, together with a tendency to overheat, led to it being rejected as a service weapon. In the 1920s it was revived, having been slightly improved in the interim. It was tested in Britain and again in the USA, but it invariably broke some component during its tests and was again rejected.

After this the Bang rifle faded from the scene. The same principle of operation by a muzzle blast cone was later used in the German Gewehr 41 rifles developed during the Second World War, but these were not

Banshee, F2D/F2H McDonnell

particularly successful and merely reinforced the earlier views on Bang's design. Although Bang was the only man to take it to any great lengths, the original idea had been suggested by Hiram Maxim in the 1880s and John Moses Browning had produced a prototype rifle of this sort in the 1890s.

It is not possible to give a data table for the Bang rifle, since each one was a unique one-off, the dimensions and calibre reflecting either Bang's current ideas or those of the particular agency interested in a test.

This Bang .303 automatic rifle was tested in Britain in 1925, but its habitual unreliability led to it being turned down

I V Hogg

Banshee, F2D/F2H McDonnell

US carrier-based fighter. The young McDonnell aircraft company of St Louis was the first in the world to receive a contract for a carrier-based jet fighter. This machine, the low-powered F2D-1 (later F2H-1) Phantom, was designed during the Second World War and proved a useful trainer to US Navy pilots in 1945-48. But it was known that the FD-1 was underpowered, and with the continued development of axial turbojet engines by Westinghouse the Navy asked McDonnell to build a more powerful fighter using two of the Westinghouse 24C engines. These later went into production at a rating of 1361 kg (3000 lb)

as the J34. The availability of this new engine enabled McDonnell to build the F2D Banshee, which became famous during the Korean war.

The prototype flew on January 11, 1947, by which time confusion with Douglas had led to the new designation of F2H-1. Under vice-president G C Covington the company design team made no attempt to be clever but instead gave the Banshee a 'straight' wing of generous area. The systems were largely electric, and the quality of airframe construction was outstanding. Features included a long and slim fuselage, electrically-folding wings, nosewheel landing gear and armament of four 20-mm M-2 cannon in the nose.

The first 56 F2H-1 Banshees for the Fleet were ordered in May 1947, followed by a contract for 188 longer F2H-2s with greater internal fuel capacity and 200 US-gallon tip tanks, the extra weight being handled by 1474 kg (3250 lb) J34-34 engines. Orders followed for a further 146 F2H-2s, of which many were F2H-2N night fighters or -2P photo-reconnaissance aircraft. Nearly all these batches were sent to Korea after June 1950 where they operated round the clock from both Navy carriers and shore bases. Air combats were few, the main tasks being interdiction and destruction of difficult surface targets.

In 1951 the F2H-3 introduced a considerable additional lengthening of the fuselage, which made possible a further substantial increase in internal fuel capacity. A major advance was the installation in the nose of all-weather intercept radar, the Westinghouse APQ-41, and another new fitting was a

flight-refuelling probe to give extended range.

The final production model was the F2H-4, in which there were many detail changes including 1633 kg (3600 lb) J34-38 engines, a Hughes radar and fire-control installation, and an extended root to the tailplane. Like the -3 model, the -4 had its cannon mounted further back and higher up in the sides of the fuselage. Production was completed at 800 in October 1953.

After an operational career that was wholly popular the Banshee began to pass out of first-line service gradually after the end of the Korean war in 1953. Owing to their docile handling and extremely good weight-lifting capability many served as trials and research aircraft, and one gained a height record for a carrier-based jet at over 15 850 m (52 000 ft).

Late in the 1950s batches of early models were used in air-to-air missile trials, while in 1956 39 ex-US Navy F2H-3s were supplied to the Royal Canadian Navy to equip two fighter squadrons embarked aboard HMCS *Bonaventure*. In 1962 few Banshees remained in US service, but the -3 and -4 models were redesignated F-2C and F-2D.

Span: (F2H-2/3/4) 13.67 m (44 ft 10 in) *Length:* (-2) 12.24 m (40 ft 2 in), (-3/4) 14.48 m (47 ft 6 in) *Gross weight:* (-2) 10 270 kg (22 312 lb), (-3/4 clean) 8618 kg (19 000 lb) *Maximum speed:* (-1) 944 km/h (587 mph), (-2 with max weapons) 856 km/h (532 mph), (-4) 982 km/h (610 mph)

Bantam

Swedish infantry antitank missile. Bantam is a conventional wire-guided antitank missile for infantry use, manufactured by AB Bofors

McDonnell F2H-3 Banshee of the Royal Canadian Navy, with lengthened fuselage and radar installation in the nose

Flight International

BAT Bantam Mk 1, one of the nine production models of the aircraft ordered by the RFC after modifications of the original machine

of Sweden and in service with the Swedish army. The missile is of the usual four-winged configuration with a hollow-charge warhead and solid-fuel boost and sustainer motors. It is supplied inside a launcher/carrier, together with a remote control unit and a 20-metre cable. The container is placed in position on the ground and the remote control unit connected. Additional cable can be connected in circuit so that the remote unit can be positioned up to 125 m (410 ft) from the launcher if the tactical situation warrants.

On pressing the firing button on the remote control unit the missile battery is activated and starts the stabilizing gyroscope. At the same time the booster rocket is ignited and the missile is launched from the container, unspooling its control wire as it goes. The wings unfold on launch, and the angled wingtips cause the missile to roll during flight. The controller, by operating a joystick control attached to an optical sight, sends signals down the wire which activate spoilers in the wing control surfaces. Due to the roll of the missile these spoilers alternately affect elevation and direction, and by use of the joystick the controller brings the missile into alignment with the optical sight and then continuously guides it to the target.

The forward section of the missile carries a shaped charge warhead which is initiated by a piezo-electric impact fuze in the nose. This fuze is electrically armed after 230 m (754.5 ft) of flight, and it is claimed that the shaped charge can penetrate 500 mm (19.7 in) of homogeneous armour plate. The minimum engagement range is governed by the arming of the fuze, while the maximum range is 2000 m (6562 ft), the length of the control wire.

Missile length: 84.8 cm (33.4 in) *Diameter:* 11 cm (4.3 in) *Wingspan:* 40 cm (15.75 in) *Missile weight:* 7.6 kg (16.75 lb) *Flight speed:* 85 m/sec (279 ft/sec)

Bantam BAT

British single-seat fighter. First flown in 1918, the Bantam was the first aircraft designed by Fritz Koolhoven for the BAT (British Aerial Transport) company. It was an exceptionally small machine, with wooden monocoque fuselage, and though it had an excellent performance on a 170-hp ABC Wasp static radial engine, it had undesirable control characteristics (notably a very difficult high-speed spin) which made it unacceptable.

After experiments to determine the cause

of the spin, a second model designated F.K.23, or Bantam Mk 1, was produced. This was more stable and nine were ordered.

Span: 7.62 m (25 ft 0 in) *Length:* 5.6 m (18 ft 5 in) *Gross weight:* 600 kg (1321 lb) *Max speed:* 206 km/h (128 mph)

BAR

US automatic rifle. The BAR (Browning Automatic Rifle), a gas-operated rifle with the bolt locked by being thrust upwards against locking surfaces in the gun body, was designed by John Moses Browning in 1915-16 and was demonstrated to US government and military officials in February 1917. After an official trial in May 1917 it was approved for issue and in July 1917 12 000 rifles were ordered from the Colt company. Other contracts were then put out to other firms, and by the end of the war some 52 000 had been made. Manufacture continued for many years both in the USA and under licence in foreign countries. The BAR made a good impression in France and it was adopted by the Belgian, Polish and Swedish armies. It remained the 'squad automatic' of the US Army until after the Second World War, and

Barbel

A GI in Germany shoulder-fires his BAR

The attack submarine USS *Barbel* (SS.580) undergoing maintenance work in dry dock

numbers were supplied to the British Home Guard in 1940-41.

Numerous variant models have appeared. The original model was intended to be fired from the shoulder or from the hip while advancing across no-man's-land, but this idea was soon abandoned and the rifle was fitted with a bipod to become a light machine-gun. Other modifications included a variable rate of fire at 'automatic', a finned barrel to improve cooling, and a monopod on the butt. US and British weapons were all of .30 calibre, those of other nations being in their own service chambering. There was also a commercial version, without the automatic fire facility, called the Colt Monitor, which was sold to police departments in the USA.

Although the BAR was a good design and well suited to mass production, it was never as successful as its designer hoped. It was too heavy to be a rifle and the bolt vibration made accurate fire from the shoulder almost impossible. On the other hand it was too light to be a good light machine-gun and was unsteady on its bipod. The small magazine meant frequent reloading, and, since it was bottom-mounted, changing the magazine when in the prone position was difficult. The barrel was not interchangeable and the gun thus heated up when fired automatic. But in spite of all this it stayed in firstline service with various armies for something like 50 years, and large numbers are still to be found in reserve service throughout the world.

(M1918) *Calibre:* .30-in *Length:* 120 cm (47 in) *Weight:* 7.26 kg (16 lb) *Barrel:* 610 cm (24 in) *Magazine:* 20 rounds *Cyclic rate of fire:* 550 rounds per minute

Name and number	laid down	launched	completed	builder
Barbel (SS.580)	5/1956	7/1958	1/1959	Portsmouth Naval Shipyard
Blueback (SS.581)	4/1957	5/1959	10/1959	Ingalls SB Corporation
Bonefish (SS.582)	6/1957	11/1958	7/1959	New York SB Corporation

Barbel

US submarine class. In Fiscal Year 1956 the US Navy was authorized to build three submarines. They were the last non-nuclear combatant boats to be ordered but they incorporated many advanced features. The hull is a 'tear drop' form, as tested in the experimental USS *Albacore*. For the first time the controls were located together in an 'attack centre', and this proved so successful that it is now standard in US Navy submarines.

The machinery arrangement is unusual, with three Fairbanks-Morse diesels driving two General Electric motors on one shaft. Mk 101 Mod 20 torpedo fire control is fitted and a BQS-4 bow sonar. When built all three had their diving planes mounted on the bow but later they were relocated on the forward side of the 'sail' or fin, as the conning tower is now known.

Displacement: 2145/2895 tons (surfaced/submerged) *Length:* 66.8 m (219 ft 6 in) oa *Beam:* 8.8 m (29 ft 0 in) *Draught:* 8.5 m (28 ft 0 in)

Machinery: Diesel/electric, 4800 bhp/3150 shp=15/25 knots (surfaced/submerged) *Armament:* 6 21-in (53-cm) torpedo tubes (bpw) (at least 18 torpedoes carried) *Crew:* 78

Barcelo

Spanish torpedo boat. Because torpedo boats had to be both very strong and very light, with (for the 1890s) high-technology engines to give them the required speed, they tended to be built by a few specialist builders in Britain, France, and Germany. Most Spanish torpedo boats were built in these countries.

In order to keep abreast of the latest developments from these firms, Spain tended to give two or three firms the same general specification, and order one boat to their own design from each firm. *Barcelo* was one of three boats ordered in this way in 1886. *Habana* was ordered from Thornycroft of Chiswick, *Orion* from Germania of Kiel, and *Barcelo* herself from the French firm of Augustin-Normand of Le Havre. All three were small 1st Class torpedo boats with a length of about 38 m (120 ft) and an armament

The Browning Automatic Rifle M1918A2, a modified version of the original M1918, with bipod attached to a flash eliminator, stock rest in the butt and cyclic rate of fire changer incorporated into the trigger guard

of two bow torpedo tubes and two 25-mm light guns.

Augustin-Normand et Cie was one of the two major French torpedo boat builders, and they had close links with the British firms of Thornycroft and Yarrow. Although they built a large number of torpedo boats for the French navy, they only built 19 boats for export, and of these only *Barcelo* was built for Spain.

In most respects she was a typical torpedo boat of the period, with two torpedo tubes mounted internally in the bows under a turtle deck forecastle. The deck was heavily cambered to the stern, and the two 1-in Nordenfelt QF guns were mounted on sponsons amidships, the port one slightly forward and the starboard one slightly abaft the single funnel. The funnel was *Barcelo*'s chief distinguishing feature, the single locomotive boiler was too tall to fit upright in the hull, and the boiler and funnel were tilted to starboard. In addition, the funnel was reduced in diameter a third of the distance from the top.

Barcelo was classed by the Spanish as a 1st Class torpedo boat, but her builders rated her as a *torpilleur garde-côtes*, and indeed her small size made her suitable only for coast defence. With her single locomotive boiler and double (rather than triple or quadruple) acting reciprocating machinery, *Barcelo* was slower than either *Habana* or *Orion*, and this may well have been a reason for the Spanish not ordering any more torpedo boats from Augustin-Normand. On a trials displacement of 63.986 tons she achieved a speed of 19.50 knots on 520 ihp.

As with all the older Spanish torpedo boats, by the time war with America began in 1898 she was too old and worn out to take any active part, and she was captured by the Americans in the Philippines in 1898 during the Spanish-American war. *Barcelo* was eventually discarded in 1911.

Displacement: 63 tons *Length:* 38.50 m (126 ft 0 in) *Beam:* 3.30 m (10 ft 10 in) *Draught:* 1.98 m (6 ft 6 in) *Machinery:* double-expansion steam reciprocating, 520 ihp=19.5 knots *Armament:* 2 1-in (25-mm) Nordenfelt QF; 2 bow 35-cm (13.8-in) torpedo tubes *Crew:* N/A

Barfleur

British battleship class. Constructed under the terms of the Naval Defence Act the *Barfleur* and *Centurion* were classified as 2nd Class battleships. They were both laid down in 1890, launched in 1892 and completed in 1894, the *Barfleur* being built at Chatham and the *Centurion* at Portsmouth. Compared with 1st Class battleships they were lightly armoured and undergunned but were faster, smaller and more economical both to build and to operate.

In many ways these ships represent an early example of battlecruiser principles as they could have operated successfully against some of the slow armoured cruisers then in existence whilst avoiding action with other battleships. Their small size was, however, more a matter of economy than tactics. They were intended for the China Station where a reasonable running cost was considered desirable together with a good radius of action and a shallow draught to enable opera-

The battleship HMS *Barfleur* photographed in 1905 after her reconstruction in 1902-04

tions in the Chinese rivers. Both were good steamers and made 18.5 knots on trial without difficulty. They were the first battleships to have hooded barbettes (the hood being the original name of what later became known as the turret) and all-round loading positions for the main armament.

Criticism of the light armament led to proposals for reconstruction and between 1901 and 1904 they were taken in hand to have their 4.7-in guns replaced by ten 6-in guns. These were mounted, five on each beam, in armoured casemates 5 in thick. This involved considerable additional weight but drastic weight saving in other areas resulted in a total addition of only 78 tons.

The *Centurion* served as flagship of the China Squadron until 1901 when she was paid off for reconstruction. She served on the China Station again between 1903 and 1905 and then returned home, where she spent most of her time in reserve until sold for scrap in 1912. The *Barfleur* served in the Mediterranean until 1898 and then transferred to the China Station until being paid off for reconstruction in 1902. She served most of her remaining time in home waters and like her sister was sold for scrap in 1912.

Displacement: 10500 tons *Length:* 109.72 m (360 ft 0 in) oa *Beam:* 21.33 m (70 ft 0 in) *Draught:* 7.62 m (25 ft 0 in) *Machinery:* 2-shaft triple-expansion steam piston engines, 13000 ihp=18.5 knots *Protection:* 305 mm (12 in) belt; 64 mm (2½ in) deck; 229 mm (9 in) barbettes; 152 mm (6 in) hood; 102 mm (4 in) casemates *Armament:* 4 10-in (250-mm) (2×2); 10 4.7-in (120-mm) (10×1); 8 6-pdr (8×1); 12 3-pdr (12×1) *Crew:* 620

Barfleur

British destroyer class. By 1941 it had become clear that British destroyers were ill-equipped to defend themselves against aircraft. The Admiralty therefore decided to produce an entirely new design for the fleet destroyers of the 1942 and 1943 construction programmes in which the principal feature was to be a substantial antiaircraft armament.

The result was the 'Battle' Class, each of which carried four 4.5-in guns in two twin dual-purpose mountings fitted forward of the bridge. The mountings were virtually small turrets, being fully enclosed, power operated, and capable of elevating the guns to 85° compared to 40° or 55° in early destroyer mountings. In addition the main armament was provided with a sophisticated fire-control system based on the new Mk VI HA/LA director with radar control and full stabilization. The remainder of the designed armament consisted of a single 4-in gun amidships, for starshell, four twin 40-mm Hazemeyer Bofors mountings, two sets of quadruple 21-in torpedo tubes, four 20-mm AA guns and a depth-charge armament.

All this, together with the speed necessary for a fleet destroyer, required a ship of comparatively large dimensions, and at over 2300 tons they were the biggest destroyers thus far designed for the Royal Navy. They were handsome ships which met most of the requirements of the Second World War but very few were completed prior to the end of hostilities. Wartime modifications to the design resulted in the substitution of single 40-mm guns for the 20-mm and the fitting of a lattice foremast.

The class fell into three distinct groups —the Early, Later and Australian 'Battles'. The Early 'Battles' were constructed under the 1942 Programme, 16 being laid down during 1942-44 and completed during 1944-46. The Later 'Battles' were constructed under the 1943 Programme, 24 being laid down during 1943-44 of which 16 were cancelled at the end of the war, the remainder completed during 1946-48. The Australian 'Battles' were improved versions of the Later 'Battles' of which two were built for the RAN during 1946-1951; two RAN vessels belonging to the same group were cancelled.

The Early 'Battles'

Only those ships completed during the war, *Barfleur*, *Camperdown*, *Armada*, *Hogue* and *Trafalgar*, carried the 4-in gun amidships which in later ships was replaced by two single 40-mm guns. The last to complete, *Cadiz*, *St James*, *Sluys*, *Saintes*, *Vigo* and *Gabbard*, mounted two twin STAAG (Stabilized Tachymetric Anti-Aircraft Gun) 40-mm AA guns in place of the 4 Hazemeyers and all the earlier units were eventually modified to this standard. By the end of the 1950s the majority carried two twin and five single 40-mm, the sixth single 40-mm on the quarterdeck having been displaced by the fitting of a 'Squid' A/S mortar. In the early 1960s the STAAGs were replaced by twin 40-mm Mk Vs in *Camperdown*, *Cadiz*, *Saintes* and *Gabbard*.

The *Barfleur* was the only one of the class to see any real war service; she took part in the final assault on Japan and was present at the Japanese surrender. In 1957 the *Cadiz* and *Gabbard* were sold to Pakistan and renamed *Khaibar* and *Badr* respectively. The *Sluys* was sold to Iran in 1966, being substantially modernized and renamed

The *Barfleur* or 'Battle' Class destroyer HMS *Matapan* in June 1973 converted to a Sonar trials ship. A 24-ft diameter sonar—reputedly the most powerful in the world—is fitted below the bows, and the after funnel is an exhaust for the turbo-generator used to power the Sonar

Artemiz. The remainder of the class were sold for scrap between 1960 and 1970. *Armada*, *Saintes* and *Solebay* were built by Hawthorn Leslie. *Barfleur*, *Gabbard*, *St Kitts* and *Trafalgar* were built by Swan Hunter. *Cadiz*, *Camperdown*, *Finisterre*, *St James* and *Vigo* were built by Fairfield. *Gravelines*, *Hogue*, *Lagos* and *Sluys* were built by Cammell Laird.

The Later 'Battles'

Although of the same basic design these ships differed in a number of particulars from the earlier class. To compensate for the lack of astern fire a single 4.5-in gun, controlled by the main fire-control system, was mounted abaft the funnel in place of the 4-in starshell gun, a US Mk 37 director was fitted instead of the original Mk VI director (owing to limited

HMS *St Kitts* (foreground) meets the cruiser HMS *Glasgow* in the Mediterranean to take on board First Sea Lord Sir Rhoderick McGrigor

manufacturing capacity for the British equipment) and quintuple torpedo tubes were substituted for quadruple. To compensate for the additional topweight the beam was increased by 3 in, which with the other modifications increased the displacement by over 200 tons.

As completed they carried a Squid A/S mortar on the quarterdeck and the close-range AA armament of all units consisted of two twin STAAG 40-mm, one twin Mk V 40-mm and two single 40-mm. During 1959 the *Jutland* had her STAAG replaced by Mk V 40-mm.

In the early 1960s the *Agincourt*, *Aisne*, *Barrosa* and *Corunna* were converted into AD (Aircraft Direction) ships, also known as radar pickets. All the torpedo tubes and 40-mm guns were removed and additional deck houses were constructed amidships. A new lattice foremast carrying a large air warning radar scanner was fitted abaft the bridge and a small lattice mainmast was added aft. A quadruple Seacat guided-missile launcher was added on the after superstructure and occasionally the ships carried two single 20-mm AA guns. The *Corunna*, commissioned in February 1962, was the first ship to carry the Seacat operationally.

During 1971-73 the *Matapan* was converted into a Sonar trials ship, emerging with a markedly different profile. The hull and superstructure were substantially remodelled, the forecastle deck being extended aft to provide a flush deck. A new clipper bow with increased flair, a modern bridge, solid foremast and a second funnel (for generator exhausts) are among the more obvious changes. The hull structure was also modified and this included the provision of a large bulbous sonar dome at the fore-foot.

The unmodified ships were sold for scrap in 1965 and of the AD conversions during the early 1970s only *Matapan* still remained in service by 1977.

Agincourt and *Alamein* were built by Hawthorn Leslie; *Aisne* by Vickers Armstrong; *Barrosa* and *Matapan* by John Brown; *Corunna* by Swan Hunter; and *Dunkirk* and *Jutland* by Alexander Stephens.

The Australian 'Battles'
The two ships of this group were ordered in 1945-46 to a modified 'Battle' design and were constructed in Australia. They differ from the previous ships mainly in carrying Mk VI 4.5-in twin turrets instead of the earlier Mk IV. This mounting, under development at the end of the war, was tested in the *Saintes* and was later fitted in the destroyers of the *Daring* Class. Like the Early 'Battles', the Australian ships were fitted with the Mk VI director. As completed they carried three twin STAAG 40-mm and five single 40-mm and unlike any other 'Battle' they carried funnel caps. In 1960 *Anzac* was converted into a training ship having all but A turret and four single 40-mm guns of her armament removed and a number of deck houses added. *Tobruk* was placed in reserve in 1960 and both vessels have since been scrapped.

Anzac was built by Williamstown dockyard and *Tobruk* by Cockatoo dockyard.

See also *Artemiz*.

Displacement: (Early) 2315 tons, (Later) 2550 tons (standard) *Length:* 115.52 m (379 ft 0 in) oa *Beam:* (E) 12.27 m (40 ft 3 in), (L) 12.34 m (40 ft 6

HMS *Barham* in February 1938 after several refits and extensive modification

Wright & Logan

in), (A) 12.49 m (41 ft 0 in) *Draught:* 4.24 m (13 ft 11 in) *Machinery:* 2-shaft geared steam turbines, 50 000 shp=35¾ knots (54 000 shp=34 knots in Australians) *Armament:* (E) 4 4.5-in (114-mm) (2×2); 1 4-in (102-mm); 14 or 10 40-mm (6×1, 4×2 or 2×2); 8 21-in (53-cm) torpedo tubes (2×4); (L) 5 4.5-in (2×2+1); 8 40-mm (3×2, 2×1); 10 21-in torpedo tubes (2×5); (A) 4 4.5-in (2×2); 11 40-mm (3×2, 5×1); 10 21-in torpedo tubes (2×5) *Crew:* 250-310

Barge, Tupolev Tu-85

Soviet strategic bomber. A smaller and lighter contemporary of the USAF's Convair B-36, Barge was the first Soviet true intercontinental bomber. It made its public debut in 1951, but the turboprop Bear and all-jet Bison were already in the pipeline and so Barge did not proceed beyond the prototype stage.

Derived from technology used in the Tu-4 Bull (copied from the B-29 Superfortress) but more than twice as heavy, Barge was powered by four Dobrynin VD-4K radial engines fitted with turbochargers and each producing 4300 hp for takeoff. Normal cruise power was 3800 hp from each engine, which drove four-bladed propellers. The Tu-85 was the last Soviet straight-winged piston-engined bomber, and it was the USSR's largest aircraft until the appearance of the Antonov An-22 transport.

Barge's trapezoidal high-aspect-ratio wings were mounted centrally on the fuselage. The fin and rudder were similar in appearance to those of the Tu-4, and the trapezoidal tailplane was mounted at the base of the fin. The main undercarriage legs retracted into the inner engine nacelles, with the nose gear retracting into the fuselage.

The bomber would have carried a crew of 16. More than 20 000 kg (45 000 lb) of bombs could be accommodated in the bomb bay, and defensive armament comprised five pairs of 23-mm NR-23 cannon in remotely controlled barbettes.

Span: 56.4 m (185 ft) *Length:* 39.3 m (129 ft) *Gross weight:* 107 000 kg (235 000 lb) *Max speed:* 660 km/h (410 mph)

Barham

British battleship. The *Barham* was a 29 000-ton battleship of the *Queen Elizabeth* Class

armed with eight 15-in and 12 6-in guns. She was laid down by John Brown at Clydebank on February 24, 1913 and launched on October 31, 1914. She was commissioned in October 1915 and served in the 5th Battle Squadron of the Grand Fleet until 1919. She was present at the Battle of Jutland in 1916 and, while in action with the German Battlefleet, suffered six hits and 63 casualties.

During the 1920s she served in the Atlantic Fleet (1920-24, 1929-30) and in the Mediterranean (1925-28). Refits in 1924-25 and 1928 resulted in the fitting of four single 4-in AA guns in place of her two 3-in AA and a new fore-top. In January 1930 she was taken in hand at Portsmouth for major reconstruction. This entailed the fitting of antitorpedo bulges which increased the beam to 104 ft, adding 4-in deck armour over the magazines and trunking the two funnels into a single uptake. She was also fitted with 16 2-pdr pom-poms (2×8), eight 0.5-in machine-guns (2×4), an aircraft catapult on X turret and two AA directors positioned on the fore-top and mainmast. In addition the bridge was modified, the mainmast was converted into a tripod and the after submerged torpedo tubes and torpedo control tower were removed. The reconstruction was completed in January 1934 at a cost of £424 000; her standard displacement at this time was 31 350 tons.

Subsequent modifications were few; in 1938 her single 4-in guns were replaced by four twin 4-in DP mountings and in 1940 a UP mounting was fitted on B turret, this being replaced by a quadruple 0.5-in gun mounting in 1941. At the same time a second 0.5-in mounting was added on the after superstructure and two eight-barrel pom-pom mountings were added abreast the bridge.

After the completion of her reconstruction the *Barham* served for a short period with the Home Fleet before going out to the Mediterranean in 1935. On the outbreak of the Second World War she returned to the Home Fleet and on December 28, 1939 while operating north of the Hebrides she was torpedoed and badly damaged by the submarine *U 30*. Repairs were carried out at Liverpool, taking three months. She later returned to the Mediterranean and took part in the Battles of Matapan, on March 28, 1941, and Crete, in May 1941. During the latter operation she was hit by a 550-lb bomb and near-missed by another during a dive–bombing attack. The

Bari

hit damaged the roof of Y turret and the near miss holed the bulge; the damage was repaired at Alexandria and Durban.

On November 24, 1941 while on patrol with her sister ships *Queen Elizabeth* and *Valiant* between Crete and Cyrenaica the *Barham* was struck on the portside by three or four torpedoes fired by the submarine *U 331*. She quickly rolled over onto her beam ends, and sank, four minutes after being struck, when her after magazines exploded. Of her crew of 1258 officers and men only 396 were saved.

See also *Queen Elizabeth* Class.

Displacement: 29 150 tons (normal), 33 000 tons (full load) *Length:* 182.88 m (600 ft 0 in) *Beam:* 27.58 m (90 ft 6 in) *Draught:* 9.35 m (30 ft 8 in) *Machinery:* 4-shaft Brown-Curtis turbines, 75 000 shp=24 knots *Protection:* 330-152 mm (13-6 in) belt; 330-280 mm (13-11 in) turrets; 280 mm (11 in) conning tower; 76-25 mm (3-1 in) decks *Armament:* 8 15-in (38-cm) Mk 1 42-cal (4×2); 14 6-in (152-mm) QF (14×1); 2 3-in (76-mm) AA (2×1); 4 3-pdr; 4 21-in (53-cm) torpedo tubes (submerged, beam) *Crew:* 925

Bari

Italian cruiser. Two cruisers were ordered for the Imperial Russian Navy from the F Schichau yard at Danzig in 1912. They were to have been named *Muraviev Amurski* and *Admiral Nevelskoi* but only the former had been launched when the First World War broke out. Both were immediately taken over for the German navy and became the *Pillau* and *Elbing*. Both ships were heavily engaged during the Battle of the Skagerrak (Jutland to the British) on May 31, 1916, but just after midnight the *Elbing* was rammed and sunk by

The cruiser *Bari*, ordered by Russia, seized by Germany in 1914 and ceded to Italy in 1920

In 1934 the *Bari* was taken in hand at the naval yard, La Spezia, for modernization including conversion of her boilers from coal to oil and reduction of power. When she emerged the following year she had only two funnels, shorter than before, and was now classed as a colonial cruiser. Despite her age she had an active war career, taking part in the occupation of Cephalonia in May 1941. At the end of 1942 she was based on Bastia, Corsica as part of the Special Naval Force, but she was laid up in January 1943 for conversion to an antiaircraft cruiser. The plans included provision of a large number of 37-mm and 20-mm AA guns, with a main armament of 65-mm or 90-mm guns.

On June 28, 1943 the *Bari* was sunk during a heavy USAAF bomber raid on Livorno (Leghorn). Salvage work started but on September 18, 1943 the Italians inflicted further damage to prevent her from falling into German hands. The hull was broken up by the Germans to clear the dock. In her last

two-and-a-half years she had steamed 6800 miles and carried out 12 missions in the North Sea and Mediterranean.

See also *Pillau* Class.

Displacement: 3248 tonnes (standard), 4390 tonnes (normal), 5305 tonnes (full load) *Length:* 135.3 m (443 ft 10¾ in) *Beam:* 13.6 m (44 ft 7 in) *Draught:* 6.0 m (19 ft 8 in) *Machinery:* (after reconstruction) 2-shaft geared steam turbines, 21 000 shp=24½ knots *Armament:* 8 149-mm (5.9-in)/43-cal (8×1); 3 76-mm (3-in)/40-cal AA (3×1); 6 20-mm/65-cal (6×1) and 6 13.2-mm machine-guns added 1940-42; 120 mines; 2 50-cm (19.7-in) torpedo tubes (broadside, above water), removed 1934-35 *Crew:* 439

Barling Bomber

US heavy bomber. The ultimate expression of US Army Air Service General 'Billy' Mitchell's ambition to build a long-range heavy bomber, the Barling is—perhaps not

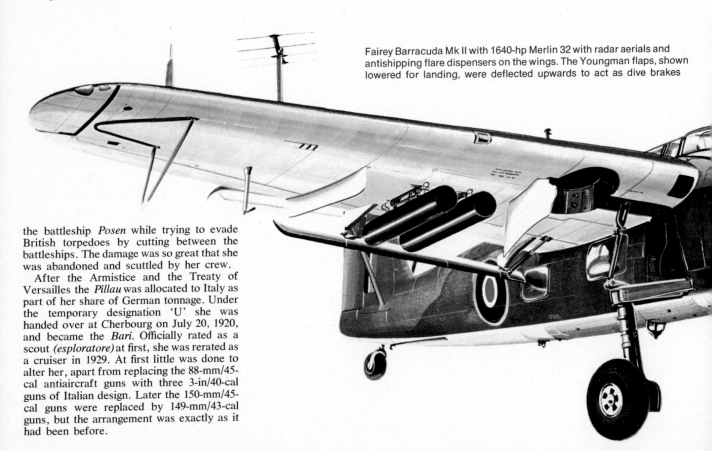

Fairey Barracuda Mk II with 1640-hp Merlin 32 with radar aerials and antishipping flare dispensers on the wings. The Youngman flaps, shown lowered for landing, were deflected upwards to act as dive brakes

the battleship *Posen* while trying to evade British torpedoes by cutting between the battleships. The damage was so great that she was abandoned and scuttled by her crew.

After the Armistice and the Treaty of Versailles the *Pillau* was allocated to Italy as part of her share of German tonnage. Under the temporary designation 'U' she was handed over at Cherbourg on July 20, 1920, and became the *Bari*. Officially rated as a scout (*esploratore*) at first, she was rerated as a cruiser in 1929. At first little was done to alter her, apart from replacing the 88-mm/45-cal antiaircraft guns with three 3-in/40-cal guns of Italian design. Later the 150-mm/45-cal guns were replaced by 149-mm/43-cal guns, but the arrangement was exactly as it had been before.

they were laid at right angles to the enemy's line of advance); however, the disadvantages of bulk, weight and awkwardness in carriage and handling outweighed this and they saw little use.

The idea was revived by the British Army in the 1960s with the development of mechanical mine-laying systems. These consisted, basically, of a plough which opened the ground, a device to deposit a mine in the furrow and a coulter to close the furrow over the mine. A circular mine demanded a large furrow and an extremely powerful vehicle to pull the plough—one early model needed a bulldozer—whereas a bar mine required a much narrower furrow and thus less horsepower.

The long and thin shape of the mine also lent itself to mechanical laying by means of an endless belt device, fed by hand from the deck of the towing vehicle. To these advantages the tactical advantage of the linear mine—which has twice the covering power of a circular mine—could be added, and the Barmine entered British service in the early 1970s.

The Barmine is made almost entirely of plastic, thus rendering detection extremely difficult, and carries a pressure-actuated fuze on its top surface. It contains 8.4 kg (18½ lb) of high explosive, quite sufficient to break any tank track and also to damage belly armour. The mechanical layer can put down up to 600 mines an hour.

Length: 102 cm (46.8 in) *Width:* 11 cm (4.3 in)
Height: 8 cm (3.2 in) *Weight:* 11 kg (24.2 lb)

Barnitzke German rifles produced late in the Second World War   See **Volksgewehr**

Barracuda, Fairey

British carrier-based bomber. Specification S.24/37 demanded a multirole bomber and torpedo carrier able to operate from aircraft carriers. The specification suggested the use of an air-cooled radial, clearly easier to maintain and better suited to arduous shipboard duty.

Fairey's Type 100, designed by M J O Lobelle, won the eventual industry competition and was as unlike the clean uncluttered Japanese machines, designed at the same time to do the same duties, as it could possibly be. It had a liquid-cooled engine, a low-rated Rolls-Royce Merlin 30 of 1300 hp (the 24-cylinder Exe, the original choice, having been abandoned). It had Youngman flaps on the mid-high wing, deflected down for landing and sharply up to serve as dive brakes.

The crew of three occupied a slim but knobbly fuselage, seated in tandem between the wing root ribs with a 'greenhouse' canopy above and large windows in the lower sides. The main landing gears had legs bent through 90° in front view and folded upwards so that the legs occupied bays in the sides of the fuselage, on each side of the pilot's seat, and the wheels were housed in the inner wings. The outer wings were folded down, back and inwards by hand, after first folding the flaps and associated structure aft of the rear spar.

The tail, not unusual today, was most unusual for that time because the horizontal

---

The monstrous Barling Bomber, described by one observer as 'more likely to antagonize the air than to pass through it,' designed by Walter H Barling,

wholly justifiably—remembered as a monster failure.

First flown by Lt H R Harris on August 22, 1923, it was a gigantic triplane, with six 400-hp Liberty engines arranged in push/pull inboard nacelles between the lower pair of wings and single tractor engines outboard. It had a biplane tail, four fins and rudders and two three-wheel landing gears, plus two wheels under the bulbous nose and a tailskid. The giant cost the then-astronomic sum of $500 000, plus a further $700 000 for its great hangar at Wright Field, in Ohio.

The design bomb load was 4500 kg (10 000 lb), carried anywhere within a radius of 1600 km (1000 miles). But early trials showed it to be overweight, and according to General 'Hap' Arnold "its performance did not come anywhere near those figures". When it was planned to fly it to Washington it was found that, with the fuel load for the 640 km (400 mile) journey, the Barling could not climb high enough to cross the modest passes of the Appalachians. It had to stay at Wright Field, where it was eventually dismantled. It was the largest military aircraft in the world in most respects until the Boeing XB-15 and Douglas B-19 of 1937 and 1941.

No data available.

Barmine

British antitank mine. The name Barmine specifically refers to the current British Army antitank mine, but it can also be used in a general sense to refer to mines which are of a linear configuration rather than the more common circular type. Mines of this shape originated during the Second World War. Their advantage lay in the greater probability of being run over by an enemy tank (provided

Barracuda, Fairey

surfaces were almost at the top of the fin. All torpedoes or bombs had to be carried externally, because there was nowhere to put a bomb bay, and the only possible defensive armament was one or two 7.7-mm Vickers K guns aimed manually from the rear cockpit. Maximum bombload was 907 kg (2000 lb), but a more usual load was a 726-kg (1600-lb) torpedo or 681-kg (1500-lb) mine.

The Barracuda first flew on December 7, 1940. After very delayed development the Barracuda I entered service with Fleet Air Arm No 827 Squadron on January 10, 1943, replacing the even less effective Albacore. The Mk II had a 1640-hp Merlin 32, with four-blade propeller, and some of this mark were fitted with ASV Mk IIN radar in a streamlined radome under the rear fuselage (again a novel apparition in 1943 but now common). A better Mk X radar installation was fitted to the Barracuda III, with the prime mission of antisubmarine reconnaissance.

Yet another new feature, standard on the III and retroactively fitted to some earlier types, was RATOG (rocket-assisted takeoff gear) for overweight takeoffs. Many 'Barras' even carried airborne lifeboats, supply containers for the Maquis in occupied France,

The Aeroplane

Fairey Barracuda Mk II. Note the unusual—for the time—position of the horizontal tailplane

and many other strange loads. Altogether 2572 of Mks I-III were built by Blackburn, Fairey and Westland. Few made torpedo attacks, but numerous dive-bombing sorties were flown, the high point of the type's career being a series of daring raids against *Tirpitz* in a Norwegian fjord by nearly all operational FAA Barracuda squadrons.

After 1945 the completely redesigned Bar-

racuda V, with 2020-hp Griffon, became available, but only 30 were delivered. The final development, the big and powerful Centaurus-engined Spearfish, did not enter production.

Span: 15.0 m (49 ft 2 in) *Length:* 12.12 m (39 ft 9 in) *Gross weight:* (Mk II, III) 6395 kg (14 100 lb) *Maximum speed:* 367 km/h (228 mph)

Barracuda Mk V, a completely redesigned version of the original aircraft powered by a 2020-hp Rolls-Royce Griffon, on board HMS *Theseus*

Flight International

Barroso

Brazilian protected cruiser class. Three cruisers were laid down at Elswick in 1895 for Brazil. Only the *Almirante Barroso* (later shortened to *Barroso*) was completed by the time the war between the United States and Spain broke out, and the other two were immediately purchased for the US Navy. The *Amazonas*, which was completed, was renamed USS *New Orleans*, and the *Almirante Abreu*, which was still on the stocks, became the *Albany*.

Almirante Barroso (No 630) was laid down in August 1895, launched on August 25, 1896 and completed in April 1897. *Amazonas* (No 631) was laid down in February 1896, launched on December 4, 1896 and completed in March 1898. *Almirante Abreu* (No 676) was laid down in December 1897 but remained on the stocks.

The ships were rather smaller than the previous Elswick cruisers and were rated as 2nd Class cruisers. The *Barroso* was refitted during 1916-17 but remained substantially unaltered throughout her life. She was discarded before the Second World War.

See also *New Orleans* Class.

Displacement: 3437 tons (normal) *Length:* 100.58 m (330 ft) pp *Beam:* 13.33 m (43 ft 9 in) *Draught:* 5.13 m (16 ft 10 in) *Machinery:* 2-shaft vertical triple-expansion, 7500 ihp=20 knots (forced draught) *Protection:* 76 mm (3 in) deck; 32 mm (1¼ in) on flat *Armament:* 6 6-in (152-mm)/50-cal QF (6×1); 4 4.7-in (120-mm)/50-cal QF (4×1); 10 6-pdr (57-mm) QF (10×1); 4 1-pdr (37-mm) QF (4×1); 4 .45-in Maxim machine-guns; 3 18-in (46-cm) torpedo tubes (above water, 1 bow, 2 broadside) *Crew:* 366

Bars

Russian submarine class. The 1912 construction programme for the Russian navy included 12 submarines for the Baltic Fleet, and six for the Pacific Squadron, all of the same type. They were designed by Professor Bubnov, the leading Russian submarine designer, but did not prove suitable in service. The Drzewiecki 'drop collars' for the external torpedoes were sited too low, on either side of the casing, where they had an adverse effect on underwater handling.

During the autumn of 1915 work started on rebuilding the class to move the drop collars higher; in some cases they were actually sited on the casing, and the later boats were completed with the improvements. After the success of the minelayer *Krab*, the *Ers* and *Forel* were altered on similar lines, but neither boat entered service until after the October Revolution in 1917.

The boats were built at the Baltic Metal Works yard at Saint Petersburg (Petrograd) and the Reval Russo-Baltic works.

As with many of the surface warships, the main machinery had been ordered from Germany, and at the outbreak of war all the diesels had been seized by the Germans. The early boats of the *Bars* Class were therefore without diesels, and it was necessary to requisition weaker machinery from the *Kopje* Class Amur monitors. Not until 1917 could 1320-bhp engines be obtained, and the first boat fitted with them, the *Kuguar*, was able to make 17 knots. Despite these problems the

Name	laid down	launched	completed	builder
Bars	1913	5/1915	9/1915	Baltic Metal Works
Vepr	1913	N/A	9/1915	N/A
Volk	1913	N/A	1915	Russo-Baltic Works
Gepard	1913	N/A	9/1915	N/A
Leopard	N/A	N/A	1917	Russo-Baltic Works
Lvitsa	N/A	N/A	1916	N/A
Pantera	N/A	N/A	1916	Russo-Baltic Works
Rys	1914	N/A	1916	N/A
Tigr	N/A	N/A	4/1916	Russo-Baltic Works
Tur	N/A	N/A	1917	Russo-Baltic Works
Jaguar	1915	N/A	1917	Russo-Baltic Works
Kuguar	1915	N/A	1917	N/A
Zmeya	1915	N/A	1917	N/A
Edinorog	N/A	N/A	1917	N/A
Ugor	1914	N/A	1917	N/A
Jaz	N/A	N/A	–	–
Forel	1914	N/A	1918	N/A
Ers	1914	N/A	1917	Russo-Baltic Works

boats completed in 1915 were active against German shipping in the Baltic.

On May 17, 1917 the *Volk* sank the steamers *Bianca*, *Hera* and *Kolga* off Norrköping. Late in May 1916 the *Gepard* was rammed by the German decoy-ship *K* while attacking a convoy, but she escaped with damage to her deck guns. During the same operation the *Bars* was also attacked but escaped without being hit. In the Gulf of Bothnia two more ships were sunk, the *Dorita* by the *Volk* on July 5 and the *Syria* by the *Vepr*.

The freezing of the Baltic prevented activity during the winter but in May 1917 the *Bars*, *Gepard*, *Vepr* and *Volk* began their patrols again. This time the *Bars* was unlucky and failed to return from a patrol. She was probably sunk by a German depth-charge attack in the Bay of Norrköping on May 28, but she could have been rammed accidentally by a Russian destroyer. The *Pantera* was damaged by an airship on June 14 and the *Lvitsa* was sunk, probably on June 11 by patrol craft. The *Vepr*, however, sank the SS *Friedrich Carow* on August 8. The *Gepard* was damaged on September 20 while carrying out an attack, and in October she failed to return from a patrol. She was possibly sunk in a minefield on October 29.

Three more of the *Bars* Class were ordered in 1911 for the Black Sea Fleet, and were known as the *Morz* Class. They were followed by a further six ordered in 1915. The launch dates for this group are not known.

The *Morz* sank a small steamer in March 1915 while the *Tjulen* torpedoed a larger

collier and 11 schooners early in April. The two boats were active again in May, when the *Morz* was damaged by a Turkish aircraft. All three were active in the spring of 1917 as well, and the new *Gagara* sank six sailing vessels on her first mission in August. The *Morz* failed to return from a patrol in May, and was probably sunk by air attack near Eregli or mined east of the Bosphorus. During the British Intervention the *Pantera* (of the original group) succeeded in sinking the destroyer HMS *Vittoria*.

Both the Baltic and Black Sea submarines of the class were victims of the chaos which followed the Revolution. The *Edinorog* was

Name	laid down	completed
Morz	1911	2/1915
Nerpa	1911	1915
Tjulen	1911	2/1915
Gagara	1915	7/1917
Utka	1915	–
Burevestnik	1915	–
Orlan	1915	1917
Pelikan	N/A	
Lebed	N/A	

Bartolomeo Colleoni

scuttled on February 25, 1918 and the *Ugor* was scrapped in 1922; the *Forel*, the incomplete *Jaz* and the *Kuguar* and *Vepr* were scrapped in 1925. The *Gagara* and *Orlan* fell into British hands at Sevastopol during the Anglo-French Intervention, and both were scuttled in April 1919. The incomplete hulls of the *Lebed* and *Pelikan* were scuttled at Odessa in 1919, and although they were subsequently raised they were not repaired. The *Burevestnik*, *Tjulen* and *Utka* followed General Wrangel into exile at Bizerta in 1920, leaving only the *Nerpa* in the Black Sea.

When Lenin gave his consent to the rebuilding of the fleet after the Civil War priority was given to submarines. The ten survivors of the *Bars* Class were refitted and given new names:

Name	renamed	renumbered
Tigr	*Kommunar*	*B.1*
Volk	*Batrak*	*B.2*
Tur	*Tovarich*	*B.3*
Leopard	*Krasnoarmeetz*	*B.4*
Pantera	*Komissar*	*B.5*
Zmeya	*Proletarii*	*B.6*
Rys	*Bolshevik*	*B.7*
Jaguar	*Krasnoflotets*	*B.8*
Ers	*Rabochi*	*B.9*
Nerpa	*Politruk*	*–*

The *Rabochi* (*B.9*) sank in the Baltic on May 25, 1931 and about July 25, 1935 the *Tovarich* (*B.3*) was rammed and sunk by the battleship *Marat* in the Gulf of Finland. Both were raised and scrapped, followed by the *Bolshevik*, *Kommunar*, *Politruk* in 1938. The remaining five boats were decommissioned before the outbreak of the Great Patriotic War in June 1941 but were used for generating power until 1945, *B.5* being renumbered *PZS.1*.

Displacement: 650/785 tons (surfaced/submerged) *Length:* 61.87 m (223 ft) oa *Beam:* 4.47 m (14 ft 8 in) *Draught:* 3.86 m (12 ft 8 in) *Machinery:* (surfaced/submerged) 2-shaft diesel/electric, 500 bhp/900 hp=11/8½ knots (early boats); 2400 bhp/900 hp=17/8½ knots (later boats) *Armament:* 1 57-mm (2.2-in) or 75-mm (3-in); 1 37-mm AA; 4 17.7-in (45-cm) torpedo tubes (internal); 8 17.7-in torpedoes (external), drop collars removed post-1925 *Crew:* 55

Bartolomeo Colleoni

Italian light cruiser. A member of the first group of the 'Condottieri' or *Alberico da Barbiano* Class, the *Bartolomeo Colleoni* entered service in February 1932 and took part in the normal peacetime activities of the Italian fleet. On November 16, 1938 she left La Spezia, bound for the Far East, and arrived at Shanghai on December 23, having called at Naples, Port Said, Massowa, Colombo and Hong Kong. She was the flagship of the Italian Far Eastern Squadron until September 1939, when the flag was transferred to the *Lepanto*. The ship left Shanghai on October 1 and arrived at Gaeta 27 days later.

The *Bartolomeo Colleoni* (under the command of Captain Catalano Gonzaga di Cirella) now joined her sister *Giovanni delle Bande Nere* in the 2nd Division of the 2nd Squadron, under Admiral Cattaneo. During her short wartime career she was to carry out six missions, two covering convoys to Africa, three in search of the British Mediterranean Fleet and one to lay mines. On July 9, 1940 she was in action against the British at the Battle of Punta Stilo, known to the British as the Action off Calabria.

By now she was under the command of Captain Novaro, who ten days later was ordered to launch an attack with the *Bande Nere* on British ships operating off Crete. The two cruisers ran into the Australian 6-in gunned cruiser *Sydney* and five destroyers. Although theoretically capable of speeds as high as 37 knots, the two Italian ships found to their dismay that the *Sydney* (32½ knots maximum) was able to keep up with them, and it was not long before the *Colleoni* was hit repeatedly. She began to burn fiercely and finally came to a dead stop, completely at the *Sydney*'s mercy. The destroyers sank her with torpedoes at about 0900 hrs, some six miles from Cape Spada.

Apart from the obviously faulty tactical thinking behind the actions of the Italian cruisers, the encounter showed that the speeds of Italian ships had been grossly exaggerated. While it is true that the class had been designed for 37 knots and had reached as much as 42 knots on trials (*Colleoni* reached 39.8 knots), these impressive figures were achieved without armament on board, in ultra-light conditions. With armament and stores aboard, the *Colleoni*'s sea speed was no more than 30 knots—exactly the same as the *Sydney*'s.

See also *Alberico da Barbiano* Class.

Displacement: 5200 tons (standard), 7000 tons (full load) *Length:* 169.3 m (555 ft 5 in) oa *Beam:* 15.5 m (50 ft 10 in) *Draught:* 4.9 m (16 ft 8 in) *Machinery:* 2-shaft geared steam turbines, 95 000 shp=37 knots *Protection:* 25 mm belt; 20 mm deck *Armament:* 8 6-in (152-mm); 6 3.9-in (90-mm); 8 37-mm; 8 13.2-mm; 4 21-in (53-cm) torpedo tubes (2×2 above water, beam) *Aircraft:* 2 *Crew:* 521

The *Bartolomeo Colleoni*, although theoretically capable of 37 knots, was caught and crippled by the 32½-knot HMAS *Sydney* in July 1940

Italian Naval Attaché

BAT

British antitank gun series. The BAT (Battalion Antitank) guns were introduced in an attempt to overcome the improved armour and reduced vulnerability of postwar tanks. Using conventional antitank guns it was found that larger and faster shells were needed to penetrate the front and sides of the new tanks, and the guns to fire these shells were far too big for infantry to move and conceal. The recoilless principle was one method of firing a large shell from a light gun, and the BAT gun was a development of a 1945 field piece.

First issued in service in 1953, the BAT was a 120-mm recoilless gun firing a 13-kg (28-lb) shell of a special design. The shell was the crux of the gun, and at the time of its introduction was the most effective anti-armour projectile known. It worked on the squash head principle, in which a thin, rounded nose flattened out on striking the target, spreading a soft mass of high explosive onto the armour. A base fuze in the shell then detonated the explosive, which gave the armour a colossal shock, all but shattering it.

The usual result was that pieces of armour flew off the inside face at high velocity and smashed around inside the target vehicle. Outside, all external items such as mudguards, aerials, bins, and even tracks and road wheels, were blown off. All glass vision blocks were shattered and even if the crew survived the flying armour pieces—which was unlikely—they were so shaken by the force of the explosion that they were incapable of further action.

Quite often these impressive results were obtained without any part of the armour being penetrated in any way. The gun needed

WOMBAT firing at night. The loader can be seen kneeling down, fingers in ears, at the side of the gun, while the tracer from the .5-in spotting rifle is visible above the barrel

was only used to keep the equipment upright when firing.

The breech was substantial and contributed 181-227 kg (400-500 lb) to the overall weight. It was a large vertical sliding block, controlled by a lever and springs, and was very expensive to manufacture. The venturi was attached to it.

The muzzle velocity of the BAT shell is only 462 m/sec (1515 ft/sec), and the trajectory is fairly high. This requires that the range to the target is clearly known, and the original BAT used a range-finder to take the range. This meant that one engagement took several minutes and a first-round hit could not be guaranteed, so in 1955 an improved

and more accurate version was designed.

The new BAT was lighter, and was called the Mobile BAT, or MOBAT. The shield was cut right down, the carriage simplified, the traversing gear abandoned in favour of hand control, and a spotting rifle fitted. The spotting rifle enabled the gunner to lay an aim on the target and judge the range and wind before he fired his 120-mm shell; this was far quicker and more accurate than the range-finder. Most MOBATs were given a .303-in Bren LMG as a spotting rifle, but trajectory did not correspond to the 120-mm round. However, it was a great improvement and the weight reduction to 764 kg (1683 lb) meant that a smaller towing vehicle could be used,

Below: **The BAT recoilless antitank gun, photographed with a round of its ammunition**

to fire these shells was at first fairly substantial, although it was far lighter and handier than the 17-pdr which it replaced.

The BAT series of guns employ the single-venturi principle of operation, using a large shell-case of conventional design with a plastic disc in the base which shatters on firing. The original BAT was built very much on normal field-gun lines and weighed 1000 kg (2200 lb). There was a small carriage fitted with two large wheels and a short box trail. The barrel was elevated and traversed by gears and hand wheels, and the crew were protected by a substantial steel shield. The towing eye was on the muzzle, and the trail

Gun	Overall weight (kg/lb)	Barrel weight (kg/lb)	Barrel length (cm/in)	Muzzle velocity (m/sec/ft/sec)	Effective range (m/yd)	Spotting method
BAT	990/2200	312.7/695	234.2/92.2	462/1515	500/545	—
MOBAT	764/1683	312.7/695	234.2/92.2	462/1515	800/872	7.62-mm Bren
CONBAT	675/1500	312.7/695	234.2/92.2	462/1515	1200/1308	0.5-in M8 Spotting rifle
WOMBAT	292.5/650	186.7/415	234.2/92.2	462/1515	1200/1308	0.5-in M8 Spotting rifle

Bat

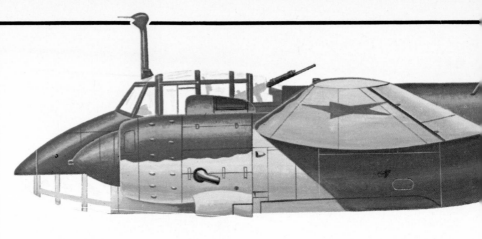

as well as a smaller crew. Even so, it was obvious that further refinements were needed and a complete redesign was put in hand.

The new gun was the WOMBAT, introduced in the early 1960s. It marked a substantial change from the earlier BATs. Only the shell and barrel design were similar; the carriage disappeared altogether, to be replaced by a light narrow frame with two tiny wheels on a short axle. There is no shield on WOMBAT and the barrel is made from high-grade lightweight steel.

The most striking changes are in the breech and the spotting rifle. The sliding breech block has been replaced by a light swinging ring which locks by rotating and carries the venturi with it. The spotting rifle is the US M8 0.5-in, taken from the 106-mm recoilless gun. The trajectory exactly matches that of the 120-mm, and where the spotting round goes, so will the 120-mm shell. The total weight of the gun is 295 kg (650 lb), less than the barrel alone of the original BAT. WOMBAT is carried in its vehicle and dismounted for action, unlike the other guns which were all towed on their wheels.

One final derivation was CONBAT, the converted BAT. It was an attempt to improve the MOBAT, and it involved further weight reduction by removing the shield altogether and fitting the 0.5-in spotting rifle. It gave MOBAT a small increase of life, but the gun was still too heavy for infantry use. The BAT series had become obsolescent by the mid-1970s and was steadily being replaced by modern guided antitank missiles.

Bat

US Navy glide bomb. One of the most successful guided weapons of the Second World War, the Bat destroyed many tons of Japanese shipping during the last year of the conflict. Operating at a time when the Japanese resorted to attacking Allied ships in the Pacific by kamikaze suicide planes, it was the complete answer to the problem of making precision hits on isolated targets at sea before the advent of effective electromagnetic jamming techniques.

Bats were operated by PB4Y-2 Privateer patrol bombers which carried one under each wing. Released well outside the range of antiaircraft fire, the glide bomb operated on a principle similar to that of live bats which give out short pulses of sound and pilot themselves by the echoes.

After flying a pre-set course under the control of a gyro-pilot, the robot Bat was guided by radar echoes from its target. The design took the form of a small high-wing monoplane with a low-set tailplane, tip-mounted fins and conventional aerodynamic controls. The radar seeker was mounted behind a hemispherical radome which gave the missile a bull-nosed appearance. The warhead, a 454-kg (1000-lb) GP bomb, mounted within the fuselage on the missile's centre of gravity, was detonated by an impact fuze.

The weapon's greatest success was in April 1945 when a Japanese destroyer was sunk at a distance of some 32 km (20 miles)—the Bat's maximum range. But not all the attacks were against sea targets. Bats effectively cut Japanese supply lines in Burma by homing onto river bridges.

The weapon was developed by the US Navy's Bureau of Ordnance under the late Hugh L Dryden who received a Presidential Certificate of Merit.

(Bat—Swod Mk 9, ASM-2). *Length:* 3.63 m (11 ft 10¾ in) *Span:* 3.05 m (10 ft 0 in) *Propulsion:* None, or solid-fuel rocket *Speed:* 480-640 km/h (300-400 mph) *Range:* 16-32 km (10-20 miles) *Warhead:* 453.6 kg (1000 lb)

The Bat US Navy guided glide bomb (above) consisted of a 1000-lb GP bomb in a plywood airframe. A gyro stabilizer maintained flight attitude while the radar transmitter and receiver in the nose locked on the target and actuated elevons on the wings to guide the missile. A Mk 122 Demolition System ensured that the intelligence system was destroyed. *Left:* Bat installed on the wing of a Privateer

Bat, Tupolev Tu-2

Soviet bomber. The Tu-2 originated in a 1938 requirement for a fast bomber able to carry all its weapons internally and drop them either in level flight or from a dive. Originally designated Samolet-103, or ANT-58, by Tupolev's design bureau, it was a twin-engined all-metal cantilever-wing monoplane.

The ANT-58 prototype, which made its maiden flight on January 29, 1941, was powered by a pair of Mikulin AM-37 12-cylinder liquid-cooled engines developing 1400 hp each. They were closely cowled to reduce drag and drove three-bladed variable-pitch propellers. The prototype's performance was impressive—maximum speed 635 km/h (395 mph), range 2500 km (1550 miles) and ceiling 10600 m (34800 ft)—but the new engines were unreliable. The second aircraft, ANT-59 or Samolet-103U, flew in May 1941 but was destroyed when an engine caught fire during flight.

The third prototype, ANT-60/Samolet-103V, therefore had M-82 14-cylinder air-

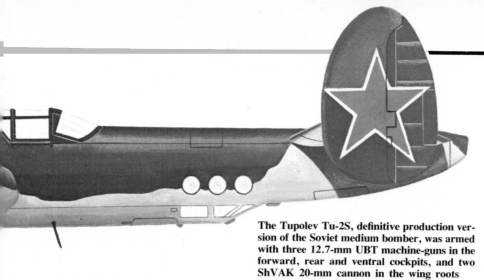

The Tupolev Tu-2S, definitive production version of the Soviet medium bomber, was armed with three 12.7-mm UBT machine-guns in the forward, rear and ventral cockpits, and two ShVAK 20-mm cannon in the wing roots

cooled radial engines installed and took to the air in December 1941, six months after the Soviet Union had been invaded by Germany. The reduction in power to 1330-1480 hp had an adverse effect on performance, but this was to a certain extent offset by better reliability. In September of the following year, three pre-production aircraft (now designated Tu-2) were delivered to a bomber regiment for combat evaluation. Enthusiastic reports of the type's abilities led to production being authorized after the design had been simplified to reduce building time.

In the definitive Tu-2S (ANT-61) the engines were ASh-82FN radials rated at 1850 hp on takeoff and 1523 hp for normal use. The aircraft carried a crew of four: pilot, navigator (who doubled as gunner and bomb-aimer), upper gunner (also the radio operator) and lower gunner. In addition to the three manually-operated 12.7-mm UBT machine-guns, each supplied with 250 rounds, the Tu-2 carried a pair of fixed forward-firing ShVAK 20-mm cannon (200 rounds each) in the wing roots. Normal bombload was 1000 kg (2200 lb) in a centre-fuselage bay; twice that could be carried under the inner wings.

Deliveries began in early 1944 but ten Petlyakov Pe-2s were produced for every Tu-2, although the latter type had a superior range and bombload. The 1111 wartime Tu-2s were, however, followed by an additional 1416 units before production ended in 1948. The Tu-2, code-named Bat by NATO after the war, remained operational with the Soviet, Polish and Chinese air forces into the 1950s and saw limited action in Korea.

Other wartime variants included the high-altitude reconnaissance Tu-2R, also known as the Tu-6, with vertical and oblique cameras, longer wings and twice the fuel capacity; and the Tu-2D (ANT-62D) having a redesigned nose as well as additional fuel. Production of the Tu-2D continued after the war. A further version was the Tu-2 Paravane, carrying a cutter for severing balloon cables.

Postwar developments included the Tu-2T, Tu-2Sh, Tu-1, Tu-8, Tu-10 and UTB (Tu-2U). The Tu-2T was a torpedo bomber tested during the winter of 1946-47. The Tu-2Sh carried a 57-mm RShR antitank gun in an unglazed nose, and the Tu-1 (ANT-63P) was developed from the wartime ANT-63 SDB as a three-seat escort fighter armed with four forward-firing ShVAK 23-mm cannon. The powerplant was two 2000-hp AM-39F liquid-cooled engines, and a bomber development was known as the Tu-10. The similar Tu-8

again had different armament and engines, ASh-82FNV radials of 1850 hp. A small number of Tu-1s and Tu-10s were built, and in 1946 Pavel Sukhoi produced the UTB (also known as Tu-2U) crew trainer with low-power engines.

The Tu-2 was additionally used widely as an engine test bed. The ANT-64 had 2000-hp AM-42 engines, the ANT-65 had a turbocharged experimental powerplant and the ANT-67 was powered by diesel engines. Standard Tu-2s were also used after the Second World War to test captured German jet engines and those supplied by Britain. These included the BMW 003 and the RD-500 and RD-45 (Rolls-Royce Derwent and Nene respectively), which were attached under the centre fuselage for trials. Yet another variant could carry a GAZ-67B command car in the bomb bay.

Tu-2S *Span:* 18.86 m (61 ft 10 in) *Length:* 13.8 m (45 ft 3 in) *Gross weight:* 12 800 kg (28 200 lb) *Maximum speed:* 550 km/h (342 mph)

Bathurst

Argentine torpedo boat class. Six torpedo boats were ordered for the Armada Republica Argentina in 1889 from the British shipbuilders Yarrow & Co, Poplar. The boats were built in 1890 and ran their trials on the River Thames before being shipped out to Buenos Aires in 1891. Their names commemorated naval heroes of the struggle for independence: *Bathurst*, *Buchardo*, *Jorge*, *King*, *Pinedo* and *Thorne*.

They were generally similar to the torpedo boats *Nos 82-87* built for the Royal Navy a year earlier, narrow single-funnelled craft with turtleback forecastles. The armament comprised a single 14-in torpedo tube built into the bow to fire ahead, and a twin training tube mounted on the after deck.

Although officially capable of 24-25 knots, like all early torpedo boats their trials were run in light conditions and smooth water, and in service they were not capable of more than 22, and even less in rough weather. The *Bathurst*, *King* and *Pinedo* were scrapped about 1914 and the others just after the war.

Displacement: 85 tons (normal) *Length:* 39.62 m (130 ft 0 in) pp *Beam:* 4.1 m (13 ft 6 in) *Draught:* 1.82 m (6 ft 0 in) *Machinery:* Single-shaft triple-expansion, 1200 ihp=24 knots (max in light condition) *Armament:* 2 3-pdr (47-mm) QF (2×1); 3 14-in (35.5-cm) torpedo tubes (1 fixed bow tube, 1×2 training) *Crew:* 15

Bathurst

Australian minesweeper class. The 60 vessels of this class were constructed in Australia between 1940 and 1944. Thirty-six were for the RAN, while 20, paid for by the Admiralty, were intended for the RN. These latter were, however, transferred to the RAN on completion. A further four units, *Bengal*, *Bombay*, *Madras* and *Punjab*, were built for the Royal Indian Navy and differed from their sisters in having a 3-in gun in place of the 4-in. Another three ships intended for the RIN were cancelled in March 1945.

The ships were of conventional fleet minesweeper type and they were generally similar in design to the RN *Bangor* Class of the emergency war programme. Although intended for minesweeping, they were often employed as escorts and patrol vessels and were frequently equipped with a depth-charge armament. They also served as transports and some members of the class even carried out shore bombardments.

During the Second World War they served mainly in Australian and Far Eastern waters, where three were lost. The first was the *Armidale*, sunk by Japanese torpedo planes off Timor on December 1, 1942. The remaining pair were lost in more mundane circumstances, both being sunk as a result of accidental collisions with merchant vessels; the *Wallaroo* off Fremantle on June 11, 1943 and the *Geelong* off New Guinea on October 18, 1944. Another unit was lost after the war; on September 13, 1947 the *Warrnambool* was sunk by a mine off the coast of Queensland.

In 1946 the *Burnie*, *Lismore*, *Toowoomba*, *Tamworth*, *Cairns*, *Ipswich*, *Kalgoorlie* and *Wollongong* were sold to the Royal Netherlands Navy and renamed *Ceram*, *Bajam*, *Boeroe*, *Tidore*, *Ambon*, *Morotai*, *Ternate* and *Banda* respectively. In 1949 the latter four of these ships were transferred to Indonesia and renamed *Banteng*, *Hang Tuah*, *Patti Unis* and *Radjawali* respectively. The *Broome*, *Gawler*, *Geraldton*, *Launceston* and *Pirie* were sold to Turkey in 1946 and renamed *Alanya*, *Ayvalik*, *Antalya*, *Ayancik* and *Amasra* respectively. In 1952 the *Echuca*, *Inverell*, *Kiama* and *Stawell* were presented to the RNZN. The *Ballarat*, *Bendigo*, *Benita*, *Whyalla* and *Gladstone* were sold into merchant service, the first four in 1947 and the fifth in 1956.

The *Bathurst* was scrapped in 1948 and the majority of the remaining ships of the class suffered the same fate during the late 1950s and early 1960s but a few survived into the 1970s as training ships.

Ararat, *Broome**, *Bunbury*, *Bundaberg*, *Fremantle*, *Gympie*, *Ipswich**, *Kiama*, *Launceston**, *Parkes*, *Townsville*—built by Evans Deakin; *Armidale*, *Burnie*, *Colac*, *Deloraine*, *Dubbo*, *Inverell*, *Latrobe*, *Lismore*, *Lithgow*, *Mildura*, *Wagga*, *Warrnambool*, *Bombay*, *Punjab*—built by Morts Dock; *Ballarat**, *Benalla*, *Castlemaine*, *Echuca*, *Geelong*, *Horsham*, *Shepperton*, *Stawell*—built by Williamstown Dockyard; *Bathurst**, *Bendigo**, *Cessnock**, *Glenelg*, *Goulburn**, *Wollongong**, *Bengal*, *Madras*—built by Cockatoo Dockyard; *Bowen*, *Cairns**, *Gladstone*, *Maryborough**, *Rockhampton*, *Tamworth**, *Toowoomba**—built by Walkers; *Cootamundra*, *Cowra*,

Battle, Fairey

Geraldton*, Junee, Kapunda, Katoomba, Wallaroo—built by Poole and Steele; Gawler*, Kalgoorlie*, Pirie*, Whyalla*—built by Broken Hill; Strahan—built by Newcastle. * RN vessels

Displacement: 650 tons (standard) Length: 56.69 m (186 ft 0 in) oa Beam: 9.14 m (31 ft 0 in) Draught: 2.51 m (8 ft 3 in) Machinery: 2-shaft steam piston engines, 2000 ihp=16 knots Armament: 1 4-in (102-mm) (3-in in RIN vessels); 1 20 mm; 4 .303-in (2×2) Crew: 60

'Battle' British destroyer class   See Barfleur

Battle, Fairey

British light bomber. When the Air Ministry issued Specification P.27/32 in April 1933 it seemed extremely advanced. It called for a two-seat single-engined day bomber able to carry a bombload of no less than 454 kg (1000 lb) at 320 km/h (200 mph) for a distance of 1610 km (1000 miles). Compared with aircraft of this class then in use it represented a leap of 100% in bombload, 60% in speed and over 90% in range.

After a lengthy gestation period the eventual winner of the industry competition appeared on its maiden flight at Northolt on March 10, 1936. It was the Fairey Battle, designed by Marcel Lobelle and outstanding for its beauty of line, elegant simplicity and tremendous performance, more than meeting the requirements. Nobody could then have suspected that this almost futuristic machine would be remembered with a shudder by a generation of bomber pilots as a sitting duck in the war that was soon to come.

Construction was entirely of light-alloy stressed-skin, a monocoque fuselage housing a crew of not two but, usually, three, under a long 'greenhouse' canopy. The usual arma-

The Royal Australian Navy's Bathurst Class minesweepers Ararat (above) and Bowen (below), photographed in 1945. Like other minesweepers, the vessels of this class were allocated J pendant numbers in 1940—the Ararat being the exception with a K pendant. The Bowen has a 40-mm AA gun aft, and a 20-mm on each bridge wing; Ararat retains her original armament

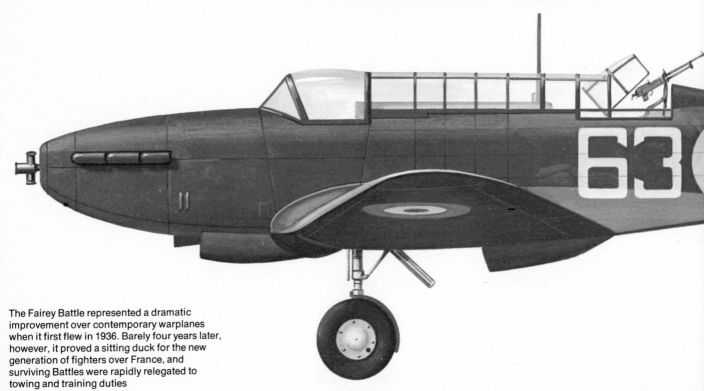

The Fairey Battle represented a dramatic improvement over contemporary warplanes when it first flew in 1936. Barely four years later, however, it proved a sitting duck for the new generation of fighters over France, and surviving Battles were rapidly relegated to towing and training duties

ment was a single .303-in Vickers K aimed from the rear cockpit and a fixed Browning of the same calibre in the left wing. The navigator/bomb-aimer could sight from the prone position in the belly, while the 454-kg (1000-lb) bombload was carried in cells inside the inner wings adjacent to the retracted main landing gears. In the nose was a 1030-hp Rolls-Royce Merlin engine, with an engine mark number the same as the airframe (I to IV), driving a de Havilland Hamilton variable-pitch propeller.

Production got under way at a great rate, as the Battle was one of the key types in the long overdue RAF Expansion Scheme, with hundreds being ordered from a new 'Shadow Factory' run by Austin Motors in Birmingham. By the outbreak of the Second World War over 1000 had been delivered, starting with No 63 Squadron RAF on March 20, 1937. Avions Fairey in Belgium produced Battles with a longer, Fulmar-like, engine radiator duct, while Fairey exported the type to Belgium, Poland, Turkey, Australia, Canada and South Africa.

When the German armies swept over the western frontiers into the Low Countries on May 10, 1940 the Battles of the RAF Advanced Air Striking Force were at once plunged into frantic action. Until then the Battle had been judged in the very front rank of combat aircraft, the more so as a Battle rear gunner on September 20, 1939 claimed the first German aircraft shot down in France. But May 1940 saw the virtual elimination of the AASF Battle squadrons.

Posthumous VCs were won by Sergeants Gray and Garland in the heroic attack on the Maastricht bridges on May 10, while on the 20th 41 Battles were shot down out of a force of 71 trying to destroy the pontoon bridges at Sedan. Within days the Battle was withdrawn from combat duty, but production continued until January 1941 when 2419 had been built

Battle converted for pilot training with two separate cockpits replacing the old 'greenhouse'

in Britain. Nearly all were then used for target and glider towing and for training, often converted with two separate pilot cockpits, in Australia and Canada. More than 60 became experimental test beds.

Span: 16.46 m (54 ft 0 in) *Length:* 12.85 m (42 ft 1¾ in) *Gross weight:* 4895 kg (10 792 lb) *Maximum speed:* 388 km/h (241 mph)

Battleaxe

British destroyer class. The *Battleaxe*, or 'Weapon', Class were constructed under the 1944 Programme but work on their design began as early as 1942. The main requirement was for a fleet destroyer which had good AA

and A/S capabilities. At the same time it was considered desirable to keep the dimensions within reasonable limits so that they could be constructed by shipyards whose slips were too small for the large destroyers of the 1942 and 1943 Programmes.

This size necessitated the adoption of the twin 4-in DP gun mounting since this was the only weapon available that would meet both the AA requirement and the weight limitation. The designed armament was six 4-in, with two twin mountings forward and one aft, two twin 40-mm Hazemeyer mountings, four 20-mm singles, two banks of quadruple torpedo tubes, four depth-charge throwers, two depth-charge chutes and 50 depth charges.

Unit machinery intended to minimize the effect of damage was adopted for the first time in a British destroyer and was arranged forward to aft in the order: boiler room—engine room—oil fuel compartment—boiler room—engine room. This arrangement required a return to two funnels, the foremost of which was led up through the centre of the lattice foremast. The result was considered by most to be very ugly and this,

The *Battleaxe* Class destroyer *Scorpion* on exercises with the Home Fleet in the Irish Sea

Bayandor

together with their light gun armament, led to much criticism of the design.

Orders were placed for 20 ships in April and May 1943 and the design was approved in June. Of these ships three were cancelled in December 1944 and 13 at the end of 1945. The remaining four were completed during 1947-48 to a slightly modified design. Two Squid A/S mortars replaced the 4-in mounting in B position in *Battleaxe* and *Broadsword* and in X position in *Crossbow*, while *Scorpion* was fitted with a single Limbo A/S mortar in place of X 4-in mounting. In addition all mounted two twin STAAG 40-mm AA mountings instead of Hazemeyers, and single 40-mm guns in the bridge wings instead of the designed 20-mm guns.

During 1958-59 all four were refitted as radar pickets, a large air warning radar scanner being mounted on a new lattice mast between the foremast and the after funnel. All the torpedo tubes were removed and in *Crossbow* and *Scorpion* the after 4-in mounting was moved forward and the A/S mortar(s) aft. Standard displacement had by this time risen to 2280 tons.

In 1962 the *Battleaxe* was badly damaged in a collision with the frigate *Ursa* in the Clyde. It was decided that her repair was not justified and in 1964 she was sold for scrap. The remaining three were sold for scrap between 1968 and 1971.

Battleaxe and *Broadsword* were both fitted as flotilla leaders and were built by Yarrow. *Crossbow* was built by Thornycroft, and *Scorpion* (ex-*Tomahawk*. ex-*Centaur*) was built by White.

Displacement: 1980 tons (standard) *Length:* 111.25 m (365 ft 0 in) oa *Beam:* 11.58 m (38 ft 0 in) *Draught:* 3.57 m (11 ft 9 in) *Machinery:* 2-shaft geared steam turbines, 40 000 shp=34 knots *Armament:* 4 4-in (102-mm) (2×2); 6 40-mm (1½-in) (2×2+2×1); 10 21-in (53-cm) torpedo tubes (2×5); 2 A/S mortars *Crew:* 234 (flotilla leaders 256)

'Bay' British antiaircraft frigate class
See *Bigbury Bay*

Bayandor

Iranian corvette class. In 1961 the United States agreed to build two frigate or escort-type warships for the Imperial Iranian Navy under the Mutual Aid programme. They were given hull-designations PF.103-104 and the order was given to the Levingstone Shipbuilding company, Orange, Texas. Five years later another pair, PF.105 and 106, were ordered from the same builder.

They resemble the Venezuelan *Almirante Clemente* Class, although smaller and slower, as they have a flush-decked hull with a marked sheer. The armament comprises two single 3-in guns, two light guns, a Hedgehog antisubmarine mortar and depth-charge throwers. A US Navy-pattern SPS-6 air surveillance radar and a navigation radar are provided, in addition to radar-direction for the 3-in guns.

No and name	laid down	launched	complete
F25 *Bayandor*	8/1962	7/1963	5/1964
F26 *Naghdi*	9/1962	10/1963	6/1964
F27 *Milanian*	5/1967	1/1968	2/1969
F28 *Kahnamuie*	6/1967	4/1968	2/1969

Displacement: 900 tons (standard), 1135 tons (full load) *Length:* 83.8 m (275 ft 0 in) oa *Beam:* 10 m (33 ft 0 in) *Draught:* 3.1 m (10 ft 3 in) *Machinery:* 2-shaft diesels, 6000 bhp=20 knots *Armament:* 2 3-in (76-mm) AA (2×1); 2 40-mm AA (2×1); 1 Hedgehog; 4 depth-charge throwers *Crew:* 140

The *Bayntun* Class frigates *Inman* (above), with the original armament of three 3-in, twin 40-mm and five 20-mm guns, and *Lawford* (below), after conversion to a Landing Ship Headquarter ship

Bayntun

British frigate class. Late in 1940 the United States Bureau of Construction began work on the design of a small DE (destroyer escort) similar in concept to the British 'Hunt' Class. It was proposed to place an initial order for 50 ships, but the final design was considered unsatisfactory and the project was cancelled early in 1941. However, in June 1941 the British asked if they could place orders with US builders for escort vessels, of which the Royal Navy was chronically short. The US agreed to this request and 50 ships based on the previously abandoned DE design were ordered. This design was chosen because the use of standard US building methods and equipment was essential and because it closely matched the Admiralty's requirements for a North Atlantic escort vessel. Despite the similarity of the ships to the 'Hunt' Class escort destroyers, the British classified the DEs as frigates.

When the United States entered the war most of the ships ordered by the Admiralty were taken over by the US Navy, but the DE programme was greatly enlarged and eventually 76 were supplied to Britain under lend-lease. Thirty-two of these vessels belonged to the *Bayntun* Class (the RN DEs were collectively known as the 'Captain' Class, being named after captains of the Nelson period), which were provided with diesel-electric machinery.

The original design provided for the installation of turbine machinery providing 24 knots with 12 000 shp, but limited turbine construction capacity led to the substitution of diesel-electric drive. This consisted of eight diesel generator sets providing power to two electric motors for the same speed. However, even the manufacture of this machinery was limited, and in order to increase the number of power plants available the number of diesel generator sets per ship was halved to four. This halved output to 6000 hp, but the resulting loss of speed was only three knots. The equivalent vessels in the US Navy were known as the *Evarts* Class and, unlike the British ships, they were equipped with torpedo tubes.

All the *Bayntun* Class were constructed by the Boston navy yard except *Drury*, which was built by the Philadelphia navy yard. *Inglis* and *Inman* were commissioned in 1944 and the remainder of the class in 1943. The intended armament, with which some earlier units were completed, was three 3-in dual-purpose guns, five single 20-mm and one twin 40-mm. However, the twin 40-mm was in short supply and several vessels mounted two more 20-mm instead. Subsequently a further six 20-mm mountings were fitted in most. Despite the substantial AA armament, they

served mainly as A/S escorts, and among the early modifications made by the British was increased depth-charge armament.

The class served mainly on the North Atlantic and Russian convoy routes, but three, the *Lawson, Dacres* and *Kingsmill,* were converted into HQ vessels for landing craft during 1943-44 and took part in the Normandy invasion. Designated LSH (S)—Landing Ship HQ (Small)—alterations included the removal of the after 3-in gun, an increase in the 20-mm armament to 16, the fitting of a mainmast and increasing radar and communication equipment.

Two of the class were damaged beyond reasonable repair, the *Goodson,* torpedoed by *U 984* on June 25, 1944, and the *Manners,* torpedoed by *U 1172* on January 1, 1945. Another four were torpedoed and sunk by enemy submarines, the *Gould* by *U 358* on March 1, 1944, the *Blackwood* by *U 764* on June 15, 1944, the *Capel* by *U 486* on December 12, 1944 and the *Goodall* by *U 968* on April 29, 1945. In addition the *Lawford* was bombed and sunk by German aircraft

Bob Burns compares his 'bazooka' noise-maker with its rocket-launcher namesake

An original pattern Bazooka—2.36-in Rocket Launcher M1—with the early (top) and late model rockets. Both types had shaped-charge warheads able to penetrate most tank armour

while operating off Normandy on June 8, 1944. The class did, however, redress the balance by sharing in the sinking of 16 U-Boats between 1943 and 1945.

During 1945 to 1947 all the *Bayntun*s, including those damaged, were officially returned to the United States, and were subsequently sold for scrap.

See also *Bentinck, Buckley, Evarts.*

Bayntun, Bazely, Berry, Blackwood, Burges, Capel, Cooke, Dacres, Domett, Foley, Gardiner, Garlies, Goodall, Goodson, Gore, Gould, Grindall, Hoste, Inglis, Inman, Keats, Kempthorne, Kingsmill, Lawford, Lawson, Loring, Louis, Manners, Moorsom, Mounsey, Pasley—built by Boston navy yard.
Drury—built by Philadelphia navy yard.

Displacement: 1140 tons (standard) *Length:* 88.24 m (289 ft 6 in) oa *Beam:* 10.66 m (35 ft 0 in) *Draught:* 2.51 m (8 ft 3 in) *Machinery:* 2-shaft diesel-electric drive, 6000 bhp=21 knots *Armament:* 3 3-in (76-mm) (3×1); 2 40-mm (1×2); 5 20-mm; 1 Hedgehog; 4 depth-charge throwers *Crew:* 156

Bazooka

American antitank rocket launcher. The Bazooka was the first completely successful one-man antitank weapon. It was a simple rocket-propelled missile with a hollow-charge warhead and an effective battle range of about 91 m (100 yards).

The designer was a Lieutenant-Colonel Leslie A Skinner of the US Army, who was a rocket engineer. In early 1942 he was trying to find a way to project a rather heavy antitank grenade that the US Army had adopted, but could not fire from any existing weapon. He fitted a rocket motor to the grenade and launched it through a tube, arranging that the motor burned out before the missile left the muzzle end. It was immediately successful, and reasonably accurate.

By good fortune the first test firings were witnessed by several senior officers and the design was adopted on the spot without further modification and ordered into production in May 1942. The popular name Bazooka was originally applied to the weapon because of its resemblance to a musical contraption of that name used by American comedian Bob Burns.

By mid-June the first 5000 had been delivered and the majority were issued to the troops going to North Africa for the Tunisian campaign. The Bazooka had its first trials in actual combat with German tanks, the Bazooka crews in many cases having learned to use it on board ship on the way. The results were amazing: several tanks exploded on being hit, the turret was blown off another and a complete troop of tanks surrendered after being shot at a few times.

The Bazooka was mass-produced throughout the war and used in every theatre and almost every battle. The Soviets were given several thousand in 1942 and put them into action immediately, losing several to the Germans who copied it in a larger version and used it on an equally large scale. Bazookas continued to be used until mid-1950 in Korea, when a combination of badly trained crews and poor ammunition caused it to fail against the Communist tanks, and it was replaced by the 88-mm (3.5-in) Rocket Launcher M20.

The original Bazooka was a simple one-piece steel tube weighing 5.8 kg (12 lb 14 oz) with the accessories. On the tube were two wooden handgrips, a wooden shoulder stock, folding sights, a wire mesh blast screen at the muzzle and a retaining clip and connecting studs at the breech end. The calibre was 59 mm (2.36 in), which was the diameter of the original grenade and warhead. Overall length was 135 cm (54 in), which made it awkward to carry in action.

The streamlined rocket had thin fins and a long pointed nose. Two wires led out from the back of the motor. The rocket was loaded into the breech end of the tube and held by the clip. The wires were led to the connecting studs and the bare ends jammed in them. The first models used a battery in the shoulder stock to provide the ignition charge, and pulling the trigger closed the circuit. The crew was two men, loader and gunner.

By 1945 the Bazooka had been improved so that it only had one handgrip, and an electrical generator in the grip provided the firing change. A reflecting sight was fitted and a light metal shoulder stock. The final improvement was to make an aluminium launch tube in two halves joined at the middle.

The Bazooka rocket had a small warhead, but it could penetrate 76.2 mm (3 in) of tank armour, and this was sufficient for most needs until 1945. It was cheap, reliable, accurate in good hands and highly effective. Although it only had a short military life the Bazooka gave its name to the whole family of shoulder-launched antitank weapons.

BC-1, BC-2 Basic combat version of North American T-6   See **Texan**

B.E.2, Royal Aircraft Factory

British multi-purpose biplane. Despite its title, the primary task of the Royal Aircraft Factory at Farnborough was not the quantity production of aircraft, but research and development. Its many-sided contribution to Britain's aerial war effort of 1914-18 included work in connection with aero-engines, propellers, bombsights and armament and considerable effort towards making flying safer. This last concern had its most significant manifestation in the B.E.2 series of biplanes, of which at least 3500 were built for the RFC and RNAS by more than 20 manufacturers throughout the British Isles. Chief among these were the British & Colonial Aeroplane company, Ruston Proctor, Vickers, Vulcan

Soldiers of the US 9th Infantry Division display the M1 (left) and M9 Bazookas. The folding M9, introduced in 1945, featured a single handgrip and light metal shoulder stock

B.E.2a, an improved version of the B.E.2, with extra engine decking and unequal-span wings

The B.E.2e, the most numerous B.E.2 variant, was developed in 1916 from the 2d. Only one pair of interplane struts connected the unequal-span wings, the large extensions of the upper wings being braced by wires from the lower ends of the interplane struts. This gave rise to rumours that the upper wing extensions would collapse under the strain of unusual manoeuvres, which, true or false, destroyed the confidence of many pilots

Motor & Engineering, and G & J Weir.

Before the outbreak of the First World War, Farnborough had gathered to itself some of the best aeronautical designers and pilots in the business; among them was Geoffrey de Havilland who, more than any other, was responsible for subsequent evolution of the B.E.2.

The letters 'B.E.' stood for Blériot Experimental, although there was no design or other connection with Blériot aeroplanes—the prefix was used simply to differentiate between aircraft with a tractor (front-mounted) propeller, as in the then current Blériot monoplanes, and those of the early 'S.E.' (Santos Experimental) type which had rear-turning or pusher propellers. (This form of differentiation was soon dropped, and the letters S.E. came to stand instead for 'Scout Experimental'.)

In 1911, Farnborough (then known as the Army Aircraft Factory) was only allowed by the War Office to repair or reconstruct aeroplanes, not to build them; but under this auspice de Havilland and F M Green so 'reconstructed' a pusher-engined French Voisin boxkite biplane which came in for repair that when they had finished it had virtually only its 60-hp Wolseley engine in common with the Voisin—and it did not keep even this for long. They named the transformed biplane the B.E.1, and it flew for the first time on January 1, 1912.

The B.E.2 appeared in the following month, as a development of the B.E.1, with equal-span, unstaggered dihedral wings, enlarged tail surfaces, a two-seat cockpit and a 70-hp Renault engine. On August 12 of that year it set a new British altitude record of 10 560 ft (3219 m). Later that month it was flown *hors de concours* during the official Military Aeroplane Competition at Larkhill, Salisbury Plain (being a 'government' aeroplane, it was ineligible for the trials), in which it demonstrated clearly its superiority over the official winner of the competition.

By this time the RFC had already placed a token order, with Vickers, for four B.E.2s, and delivery of these began in February 1913. Other orders followed during that year, mostly for the B.E.2a version, which had unequal-span wings, extra front-cockpit decking and a modified fuel system. At least three RFC squadrons were equipped with these aircraft by the outbreak of war, and others were formed very shortly afterwards, using also the slightly improved B.E.2b.

The first British aircraft to land in France after the outbreak of war was a B.E.2a, an aircraft of No 2 Squadron, RFC, which arrived there on August 13, 1914. Another officer of No 2 Squadron, Lt W B Rhodes-Moorhouse, became the war's first air VC when, on April 26, 1915, although seriously wounded, he brought his B.E.2 safely back to base after a bombing attack on the railway station at Courtrai.

These early B.E.2 versions usually carried no fixed armament, their sole defence being rifles or revolvers taken on board by their observers. They could, however, carry three small bombs or a single 45-kg (100-lb) bomb under the fuselage, and the RNAS in particular used them for light bombing.

Mention has been made of the Royal Aircraft Factory's concern with flight safety. It took the view, quite rightly, that the safest aeroplane to fly was one that was inherently stable in the air. Therefore, thanks largely to some exhaustive test flying done by the Factory's test pilot Edward Busk, the next variant, the B.E.2c, was a much more stable machine. It had aileron controls instead of the former wing-warping, staggered wings, a 90-hp RAF 1a engine (eventually), a defensive machine-gun in the front (observer's) cockpit, and could carry 10 9-kg (20-lb) or two 51-kg (112-lb) bombs under the wings.

Unfortunately, what the designers failed to appreciate, or had chosen to ignore, was that the more stability built into the aeroplane, the more difficult it was to manoeuvre. Desirable though this stability was for an aircraft intended for bombing and reconnaissance missions, it also made the luckless B.E.2c a sitting duck for enemy fighters, especially the front-gunned 'Eindeckers' (Fokker E types) which appeared in 1915. It was too stable to outmanoeuvre them, too slow to outpace or outclimb them, and too poorly armed to offer much effective resistance.

Despite its appalling combat reputation as 'Fokker fodder', however, the B.E.2c was still a more efficient bombing and reconnaissance aircraft than the earlier versions. It entered service in April 1915, was maintained in production at a high rate, and was still serving on the Western Front in 'Bloody April' two years later. At home, flown as a

B.E.8, Royal Aircraft Factory

single-seater from the rear cockpit, the B.E.2c was particularly effective as a home defence fighter, its stability making it a good gun-firing platform for night fighting in particular.

In 1916 it was followed by the B.E.2d, which at last adopted a more logical (and more effective) seating arrangement with the pilot in front and the observer behind. A forward-firing Vickers machine-gun was added to the defensive armament, the observer having a free-firing Lewis for rearward defence. The B.E.2d could carry the same bombload as the B.E.2c over a longer range, but its climb rate was only half that of the B.E.2c (which itself took 45 minutes to reach its modest ceiling of 3050 m (10 000 ft).

The final version was also the most widely built. This was the B.E.2e, which inexplicably reverted to a pilot-at-the-back layout. Like the B.E.2d, its climb rate was inferior to that of the B.E.2c, though its level speed was slightly higher and it was lighter on the controls.

It is impossible to give precise production figures, but approximately 200 of the early B.E.2/2a/2b series were built, approximately 1300 examples of the B.E.2c/2d, and about 1800 of the B.E.2e. By far the greater proportion of these were used by the RFC, but smaller quantities served also with the RNAS; a few B.E.2ds, fitted with 150-hp Hispano-Suiza engines, were supplied to the Belgian air force; and 12 B.E.2es were purchased by the US Navy for use as trainers. In addition to service on the Western Front, the B.E.2 series also served in the Mediterranean/Middle Eastern area, including the Aegean, the Dardanelles, Macedonia and North Africa, where the lack of effective opposition prolonged their useful lives.

(B.E.2c, RAF 1a engine) *Span:* 11.28 m (37 ft 0 in) *Length:* 8.31 m (27 ft 3 in) *Gross weight:* 972 kg (2142 lb) *Max speed:* 116 km/h (72 mph)

B.E.8, Royal Aircraft Factory

British reconnaissance and training aircraft. Entering service with the Royal Flying Corps in May 1914, the B.E.8 was an equal-span, two-bay biplane with a wing-warping system of lateral control. It was powered by an 80-hp Gnome engine, and was used initially for unarmed reconnaissance and liaison, carrying a two-man crew seated in tandem.

The B.E.8 was the sixth and last Royal Aircraft Factory design to have a rotary engine, and the only one of these to be produced in quantity; later in the First World War some were refitted with 80-hp Clerget or 100-hp Gnome Monosoupape rotaries. Farnborough completed only the two prototypes (in 1912) and one other B.E.8 (1913), production aircraft being built by the British & Colonial Aeroplane Company (6) and Vickers (11). They were followed in March 1915 by the B.E.8a (for training only: shorter-span wings, with ailerons), of which Vickers delivered 24 and Coventry Ordnance Works 14.

Small numbers of B.E.8s went to France with the RFC in 1914 but their achievements were not particularly notable.

Span: 12.04 m (39 ft 6 in) *Length:* 8.31 m (27 ft 3 in) *Gross weight:* 839 kg (1850 lb) approx *Maximum speed:* 113 km/h (70 mph)

Above: **Production B.E.2c, photographed here in 1915**

B.E.2a. A machine of this type was the first British aircraft to land in France on the outbreak of the First World War, but during 1915 the early B.E.2s were rapidly outclassed

B.E.12, Royal Aircraft Factory

British general-purpose aircraft. Evolved initially by converting a B.E.2c airframe, fitting a more powerful engine (the 150-hp RAF 4) and blanking off the front cockpit, the B.E.12 was first flown in mid-1915. It entered RFC service about a year later, its first employment being as a single-seat fighter with a Lewis machine-gun strapped on each side of the cockpit and firing outward at an angle to clear the propeller blades.

Since the B.E.2c's main weakness was its lack of manoeuvrability, and the B.E.12 manoeuvred even more slowly, this was a predictable failure, aggravated further by the need to fly the aircraft crabwise in order to aim the guns. Losses were equally heavy when the B.E.12 was used subsequently as a light bomber, carrying 12 or 16 7.25-kg (16-lb) or two 50-kg (112-lb) bombs.

By mid-1917 it had been withdrawn from the Western Front, but it gave useful service in the Middle East and with RFC home defence squadrons. Variants included the improved B.E.12a (single-bay B.E.2e wings), which was easier to control and land; and the 1917 B.E.12b, produced for home defence to

Above: B.E.2cs on a desert airfield in Mesopotamia, where the lack of opposition prolonged their useful lives. *Below:* B.E.8 at Upavon in 1914. Dubbed the 'Bloater' because of its bull-nose, this was the last of the B.E. series—and the last Farnborough design—to have a rotary engine

Beagle

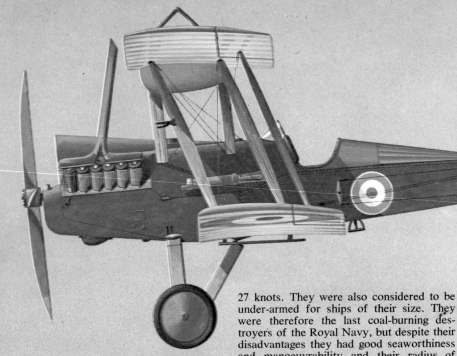

intercept Zeppelins and powered by the much-sought-after 200-hp Hispano-Suiza 8 Ac engine. One of No 37 Squadron's aircraft shot down Zeppelin *L 48* on June 17, 1917.

Various armament permutations included overwing upward-firing twin Lewis guns; synchronized forward-firing Vickers and Lewis guns; a single rearward-firing Lewis; and Le Prieur air-to-air rockets mounted on the outer interplane struts. Production orders totalled 600 (500 by Daimler, 50 each by Standard Motors and Coventry Ordnance Works), including nearly 100 B.E.12as and 115 or more B.E.12bs.

(B.E.12) *Span:* 11.28 m (37 ft 0 in) *Length:* 8.31 m (27 ft 3 in) *Gross weight:* 1067 kg (2352 lb) *Maximum speed:* 164 km/h (102 mph)

Be-12 Soviet (Beriev) aircraft   See **Mail**

Beagle

British destroyer class. In the 34-knot 'Tribal', or *Cossack*, Class of the 1905-08 Programmes, coal-fired boilers had been abandoned in favour of oil-fired. This gave advantages in both performance and convenience, but the Admiralty was seriously concerned about the supply of this fuel which, unlike coal, came from abroad along vulnerable lines of supply. Reports that German destroyers were achieving speeds of 34 knots using coal convinced the Admiralty that a return to coal was both desirable and practical. The *Beagle* Class destroyers of the 1908-09 Programme were therefore designed with five coal-burning boilers, but, despite being larger than the 'Tribals' and contemporary German ships, their designed speed was only 27 knots. They were also considered to be under-armed for ships of their size. They were therefore the last coal-burning destroyers of the Royal Navy, but despite their disadvantages they had good seaworthiness and manoeuvrability and their radius of action was generally better than that of the 'Tribals'.

The designed armament was five 12-pdrs, two on the forecastle, two in echelon amidships and one aft, but prior to completion the two forecastle guns were replaced by a single

4-in. They were the first destroyers to mount 21-in torpedo tubes, two of which were mounted on the centreline aft, one being unsatisfactorily on the extreme stern.

The 16 ships of the class were completed during 1910-11 and joined the Home Fleet. In 1912 they were transferred to the Mediterranean and, apart from a short period at the end of 1914 when six were operating in home waters, remained there until 1917. During this time they were in action at the Dardanelles and Gallipoli. In 1917 they returned home and joined the 2nd Flotilla based in Northern Ireland and were employed mainly on escort and patrol work. For this purpose they were equipped with depth charges and throwers and a few had their aftermost torpedo tube replaced by an AA gun. Some of the class were subsequently transferred to the Tees and Devonport for similar duties.

. Three of the class were lost, all by accident. The *Wolverine* sank after a collision with the sloop *Rosemary* off Northern Ireland on December 12, 1917; the other two were wrecked in 1918, the *Racoon* on the coast of Northern Ireland on January 9, and the *Pincher* on the Seven Stones on July 24. The remaining ships of the class were sold for scrap during 1920-21. Admiral of the Fleet Viscount Cunningham of Hyndhope, C-in-C Mediterranean Fleet during the Second World War, commanded the *Scorpion* from 1911 until 1918.

The B.E.12 (above) was developed from the B.E.2c in 1916 in response to RFC requests for a single-seat fighter to combat the Fokker menace. It was armed with a single synchronized Vickers on the port side of the fuselage, as here, or two Lewis guns, one on either side of the fuselage on Strange mountings, angled outwards to clear the arc of the propeller, or a combination of one Vickers and one Lewis

Basilisk, Harpy—built by White; *Beagle, Bulldog, Foxhound*—built by John Brown; *Grampus* (ex-*Nautilus*)—built by Thames Iron Works; *Rattlesnake*—built by London and Glasgow; *Scourge*—built by Hawthorn Leslie; *Grasshopper, Mosquito, Scorpion* —built by Fairfield; *Pincher*—built by Denny; *Racoon, Renard, Wolverine*—built by Cammell Laird; *Savage*—built by Thornycroft.

Displacement: 897 to 975 tons *Length:* 83.82 m (275 ft 0 in) oa, average *Beam:* 8.38 m (27 ft 6 in) *Draught:* 2.59 m (8 ft 6 in) *Machinery:* 3-shaft, steam turbines 14 300 shp=27 knots *Armament:* 1 4-in (102-mm); 3 12-pdr (3×1); 2 21-in (53-cm) torpedo tubes *Crew:* 96

Beagle

British destroyer class. The *Beagle*, or 'B' Class, destroyers of the 1928 Programme were of the same design as the *Acasta* Class of the previous year's programme. There were, however, some minor differences, principally the fitting of Asdic and an increase in the depth-charge armament. All eight vessels were laid down in 1929, launched in 1930 and completed in 1931.

The class became the 4th Destroyer Flotilla and served in the Mediterranean Fleet until 1936 when it transferred to the Home Fleet. In 1939 all except *Bulldog*, which served in the Mediterranean and Far East during 1939-40, joined the 19th Destroyer Flotilla at

HMS *Bulldog* (left), of the second *Beagle* Class, before modifications for escort work were carried out, with all four 4.7-in guns still mounted. Virtual repeats of the 'A' or *Acasta* Class, the destroyers of this class were bound by the terms of the Washington Treaty and were not competitive with the contemporary French 'contre-torpilleurs'

Beagle

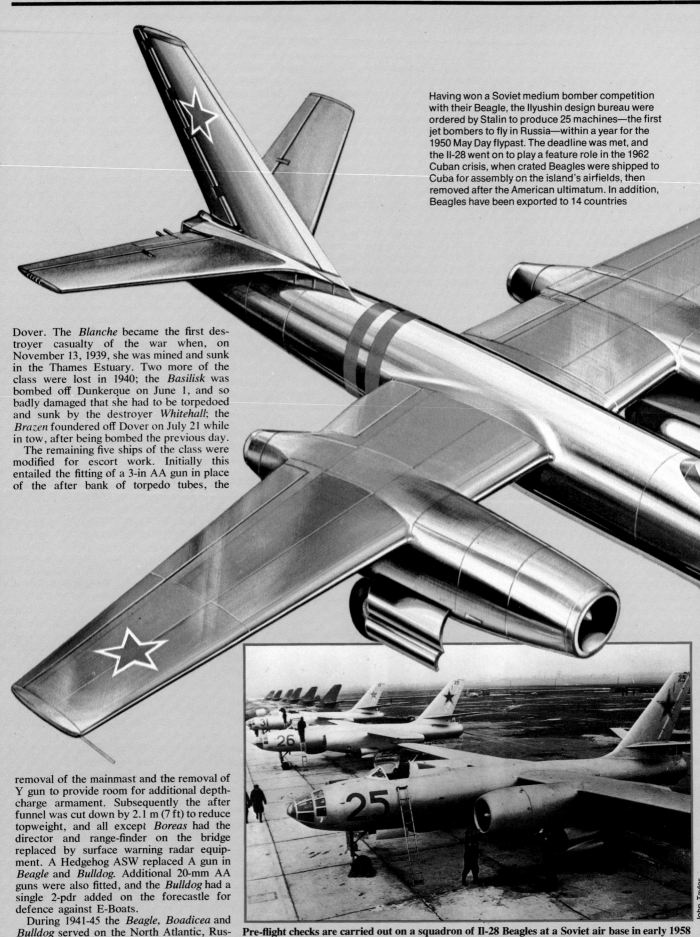

Having won a Soviet medium bomber competition with their Beagle, the Ilyushin design bureau were ordered by Stalin to produce 25 machines—the first jet bombers to fly in Russia—within a year for the 1950 May Day flypast. The deadline was met, and the Il-28 went on to play a feature role in the 1962 Cuban crisis, when crated Beagles were shipped to Cuba for assembly on the island's airfields, then removed after the American ultimatum. In addition, Beagles have been exported to 14 countries

Dover. The *Blanche* became the first destroyer casualty of the war when, on November 13, 1939, she was mined and sunk in the Thames Estuary. Two more of the class were lost in 1940; the *Basilisk* was bombed off Dunkerque on June 1, and so badly damaged that she had to be torpedoed and sunk by the destroyer *Whitehall*; the *Brazen* foundered off Dover on July 21 while in tow, after being bombed the previous day.

The remaining five ships of the class were modified for escort work. Initially this entailed the fitting of a 3-in AA gun in place of the after bank of torpedo tubes, the removal of the mainmast and the removal of Y gun to provide room for additional depth-charge armament. Subsequently the after funnel was cut down by 2.1 m (7 ft) to reduce topweight, and all except *Boreas* had the director and range-finder on the bridge replaced by surface warning radar equipment. A Hedgehog ASW replaced A gun in *Beagle* and *Bulldog*. Additional 20-mm AA guns were also fitted, and the *Bulldog* had a single 2-pdr added on the forecastle for defence against E-Boats.

During 1941-45 the *Beagle, Boadicea* and *Bulldog* served on the North Atlantic, Rus-

Pre-flight checks are carried out on a squadron of Il-28 Beagles at a Soviet air base in early 1958

John Taylor

Standard production Il-28s in service with the Soviet Frontal Aviation (*Frontovaya Aviatsiya*) in early 1958

John Taylor

The *Beagle* and *Bulldog* were sold for scrap in 1946 and the *Brilliant* in 1948. The *Boreas* was loaned to Greece in 1944; she was returned in 1951 and sold for scrap in the following year.

Basilisk, Beagle—built by John Brown; *Blanche, Boadicea*—built by Hawthorn Leslie; *Boreas, Brazen*—built by Palmers; *Brilliant, Bulldog*—built by Swan Hunter.

Displacement: 1360 tons (standard) *Length:* 98.45 m (323 ft 0 in) oa *Beam:* 9.83 m (32 ft 3 in) *Draught:* 2.59 m (8 ft 6 in) *Machinery:* 2-shaft geared steam turbines, 34 000 shp=35 knots *Armament:* 4 4.7-in (120-mm) (4×1); 2 2-pdr (2×1); 8 21-in (53-cm) torpedo tubes (2×4) *Crew:* 138

Beagle Ilyushin Il-28

Soviet light/medium bomber. The Beagle made its maiden flight on August 8, 1948, and entered service about two years later as the first operational Soviet jet bomber. Stalin had ordered that 25 should be available for Moscow's 1950 May Day flypast, and up to 10 000 have since been built in the Soviet Union and Czechoslovakia (as the B-228). Between 800 and 1000 have been exported to Afghanistan, Algeria, Cuba (withdrawn after the 1962 crisis), East Germany, Hungary, Indonesia, Nigeria, North Korea, North Vietnam, Poland, Romania, Egypt, China and Finland. Unarmed Beagles have been used for meteorological flights, and the two-seat Il-28U Mascot trainer, which first appeared in 1951, has also been exported.

The Beagle, roughly equivalent to the English Electric Canberra, is an all-metal

shoulder-wing aircraft powered successively by two RD-45s (Rolls-Royce Nenes), RD-45FAs and VK-1s. The last-named turbojet has a thrust of 2700 kg (5952 lb). The engines are mounted under the wings in nacelles developed on the experimental Tu-77. The crew of three comprises a pilot, navigator (who also acts as bomb-aimer) and radio-operator/rear gunner. The glazed nose contains a bombsight originally developed in Germany, and a radar for navigation and blind bombing is mounted under the chin.

Defensive armament is made up of two 20-mm or 23-mm cannon in the sides of the forward fuselage and a further pair in a rear turret. The rear gun installation is derived from that used in the B-29/Tu-4. There is no radar director for the rear guns, but later Beagles incorporated tail-warning radar. Up to 1000 kg (2205 lb) of bombs can be carried in the central bay, and 7900 litres (1740 gal) of fuel is contained in five flexible tanks surrounding this bay. Additional fuel can be carried in wing-tip tanks.

Ejection seats are provided for the navigator and pilot, the latter sitting under a fighter-type canopy, and the rear gunner has an escape chute. The crew compartments are pressurized.

Additional variants include the Soviet Navy's Il-28T torpedo bomber, which had larger radomes under the fuselage and was employed in the Baltic and Black Sea, and the reconnaissance Il-28R. This latter version could carry optical cameras or electronic surveillance equipment in the bomb bay, and some examples had two radar bulges in that position. The Il-28U Mascot, mentioned above, has a second cockpit in place of the navigator's position and carries no radar or

sian and Channel convoy routes while the *Boreas* and *Brilliant* operated in the South Atlantic. The *Boadicea* was torpedoed and sunk by German aircraft on June 13, 1944 while on convoy duty off Portland. The class claimed three U-Boats; the *Brazen*, assisted by the destroyer *Fearless*, sank *U 49* off Norway on April 15, 1940; the *Beagle*, assisted by carrier aircraft, sank *U 355* during the passage of Russian convoy *JW58* on April 1, 1944; and the *Bulldog* sank *U 719* north-west of Ireland on June 26, 1944. In addition the *Brilliant* sank the Vichy French sloop *La Surprise* in the Atlantic on August 11, 1942.

Bear

armament. The Finnish air force uses its Beagles as target tugs, and a commercial version, the Il-20, served with Aeroflot before the introduction of the Tu-104.

Span: 21.45 m (70 ft 4 in) *Length:* 17.65 m (57 ft 11 in) *Gross weight:* 21 000 kg (46 300 lb) *Maximum speed:* 900 km/h (560 mph) with 1000 kg (2205 lb) bombload

Bear, Tupolev Tu-95 (Tu-20)

Soviet strategic bomber and reconnaissance aircraft. With the recent retirement of the Tu-114 Rossiya airliner, the Bear is the world's only turboprop-powered aircraft with swept wings. The bomber and commercial transport bore the same relationship to each other as

Bear-C maritime surveillance version of the Tu-20 (right), and Bear-D antishipping missile control aircraft over USS *John F Kennedy*

did the Tu-16 Badger and Tu-104, the airliner having a larger fuselage with the wing mounted low on it rather than centrally.

The Bear made its maiden flight in the summer of 1954 and was displayed publicly at Tushino during the following July. Deliveries to the Soviet Air Force's *Aviatsiya Dalnovo Deistviya* (Long-Range Aviation) began in 1957, and *Morskovo Aviatsiya* (Naval Aviation) received its first aircraft four years later. The total production is believed to have been about 300 Bears, designated Tu-95 by the Tupolev design bureau and Tu-20 by the armed forces.

The Bear was designed as an intercontinental strategic bomber to succeed the Tu-4 Bull (a copy of the Boeing B-29 Superfortress). The Myasishchev Mya-4 Bison also resulted from this requirement, but the piston-engined Tu-85 and turbine Ilyushin Il-46 did not proceed beyond the prototype stage. The Bear is thus the Soviet equivalent of the B-52 Stratofortress operated by the USAF's Strategic Air Command, although the two types are vastly different.

The Bear is powered by four Kuznetsov NK-12 turboprops, rated at 12 000 equivalent horse-power in early variants and subsequently uprated to 14 795 ehp as the NK-12MV. The engine, having a 14-stage compressor, annular combustion chamber and five-stage axial turbine, was originally developed between 1950 and 1954 by a team of former Junkers engineers. The Bear was

designed for a maximum speed of Mach 0.85 at 11 000 m (30 000 ft), with the propellers turning at 750 rpm and having a tip speed of Mach 1.08. The units of 5 m (16 ft 5 in) diameter used at first have since been replaced by the Type AV-60N propeller, 5.6 m (18 ft 5 in) across and with a tip speed substantially above that of sound. The pitch of the eight-blade contra-rotating propellers is automatically varied in flight and can be reversed to provide braking on landing.

Six variants of the Bear have been identified by NATO, and all remained in service in early 1977. The original Bear-A can carry 11 300 kg (25 000 lb) of bombs internally and has a range of 12 500 km (7800 miles) with this payload. The crew of at least ten includes two pilots, one or two navigators, an engineer, radar operators and gunners. Defensive armament is reported to consist of a forward-firing fixed NR-23 23-mm cannon in the starboard side of the nose, twin weapons of the same type in a remotely controlled ventral barbette and a further twin mounting in a manned tail turret. The movable guns are directed by radar and the barbette can be sighted from glazed blisters

One of the fastest ever piston-engined fighters, the Grumman F8F Bearcat was designed to have the smallest possible airframe that would accommodate the big Double Wasp radial. Although the Bearcat entered squadron service just too late to see combat during the Second World War, many served with the French in Indo-China, and subsequently with the Vietnamese and Thai air forces

on either side of the rear fuselage. Other sources make no reference to a fixed cannon, but list Bear-A as having an additional dorsal barbette containing twin 23-mm weapons.

In Bear-B a nose-mounted radar replaces the chin radar and glazed bomb-aimer's position, and the offensive armament is a single turbojet-powered AS-3 Kangaroo long-range air-to-surface missile carried partially recessed in the bomb bay. The defensive armament is retained, although there is confusion between sources as to whether the dorsal barbette contains one or two cannon. Bear-B carries a flight-refuelling nose probe as standard and is now used mainly for maritime patrol.

Bear-C is similar to the previous variant, apart from minor differences, but Bear-D returns to a glazed nose and chin-mounted J-band Short Horn bombing and navigation radar. A major difference, however, is the introduction of a belly-mounted X-band search radar used to find targets for air-to-surface and surface-to-surface missiles launched over the radar horizon. Information displayed by this radar is transmitted by data link to the launch aircraft, ship or shore station. A Bee Hind I-band tail-warning radar is fitted as standard, and fairings on the tailplane tips are believed to house ECM (electronic countermeasures) equipment.

Bear-E is similar to Bear-A and can carry six or seven reconnaissance cameras in the fuselage. The most recent variant is Bear-F, which has aerodynamic fairings on the rear of the inboard engine nacelles. The belly radar is smaller and mounted further forward than in Bear-D, and a modified chin radar is carried by some aircraft. The forward fuselage is also longer, and there are two weapon bays in the rear fuselage. One of these replaces the ventral barbette, leaving the rear turret as the sole defensive armament.

The Tu-126 Moss airborne command post is based on the Tu-114 airliner rather than on Bear, but the long-range civil Tu-114D is in fact a Bear with the armament removed and windows provided in the basic bomber fuselage. However, only a small number of this version were built.

Span: 48.5 m (159 ft 0 in) *Length:* 47.5 m (155 ft 10 in) *Gross weight:* 155 000 kg (340 000 lb) *Maximum speed:* 805 km/h (500 mph)

Bearcat, F8F Grumman

American carrier-based fighter. In 1943 the US Navy, like the Army Air Force, became interested in the possibility of lighter and smaller fighters able to achieve higher performance with available engines. Though the large Hellcat and Corsair remained in full production as the standard carrier-based fighters, Grumman Aircraft were assigned the task of preparing a completely new design, using the same engine as in the two big fighters, the 2400-2800-hp Pratt & Whitney R-2800 Double Wasp radial. Prototypes of the new 'lightweight fighter', the XF8F, were ordered on November 27, 1943, and the first flew on August 21, 1944.

Compared with the F6F Hellcat, the F8F-1 Bearcat was similar in layout but markedly smaller, and it had a teardrop canopy and wide-track landing gears retracting inwards. Its outstanding pilot view, large flaps and

Beardmore-Farquhar

John Taylor

The F8F-2 version of the Bearcat (above) had a taller tailfin and redesigned engine cowling and was armed with four wing-mounted cannon

excellent control at low air speeds made it highly suitable for carrier use, and despite structural strength even greater than that of the F6F it had an airframe approximately 900 kg (2000 lb) lighter. Only the tips of the wings folded, and four 12.7-mm (0.50-in) Browning guns were housed in the fixed portion beyond the landing gears and propeller disc. Acceleration, with 2800 hp and a propeller with four broad blades, exceeded that of any previous fighter, and for the first time the pilot was seated in a semi-reclining position, with feet high, to increase tolerance to g in turns.

Development was rapid, and deliveries began on December 1, 1944. By 1945 both Grumman, building the F8F-1, and Eastern Motors (division of General Motors), making the F3M-1, were producing in quantity, and squadron VP-19 was nearing operational status. After VJ-Day Eastern's contract was cancelled, but Grumman went on to build 765 F8F-1s, 100 -1Bs with four 20-mm M2 cannon, 36 -1Ns with APS-6 radar on a wing pod, 293 -2s with taller fin and other changes, and 60 -2P long-range reconnaissance Bearcats with only two guns. All fighter versions could carry two drop tanks, or 454-kg (1000-lb) bombs, or equivalent loads of rockets.

Most Bearcat units had re-equipped with Banshee or Phantom jets by the Korean war, but over 250 modified examples served with the French in Indo-China during 1952-56 and survivors finished their days in Vietnam and Thailand during 1956-66. Several are still airworthy, one of them a specially rebuilt racer belonging to Darryl F Greenamyer who flew it to a new world piston-engined speed record at 776 km/h (482.5 mph) in 1969.

(F8F-2) *Span:* 10.7 m (35 ft 6 in) *Length:* 8.43 m (27 ft 8 in) *Gross weight:* 6120 kg (13 494 lb) *Maximum speed:* 720 km/h (447 mph)

Beardmore-Farquhar

British aircraft observer's machine-gun. This gun was designed during the First World War by Colonel Mowbray G Farquhar of Aboyne, Aberdeenshire, a designer who had previously produced an automatic rifle which came very close to service acceptance. He entered into an agreement with the Beard-

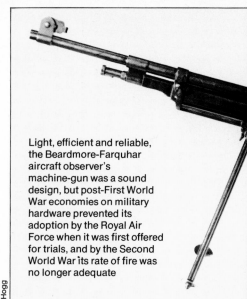

I V Hogg

Light, efficient and reliable, the Beardmore-Farquhar aircraft observer's machine-gun was a sound design, but post-First World War economies on military hardware prevented its adoption by the Royal Air Force when it was first offered for trials, and by the Second World War its rate of fire was no longer adequate

more engineering company of Birmingham and a number of guns were produced and submitted for test by the RAF in 1919.

The gun was gas operated, but instead of the usual mechanism in which a gas piston operates directly on the bolt, in Farquhar's design the gas piston compressed a spring which in turn bore against the bolt. While gas pressure in the gun chamber remained high, the bolt remained locked, but as soon as pressure dropped to a safe level the power of the compressed spring could unlock the bolt and drive it back to begin the usual cycle of extracting and feeding. Due to the interpolation of the spring, the action was remarkably smooth and free from vibration, and stoppages were extremely rare. Moreover, since the action was smooth, the gun could be made lighter, and it weighed only 7.4 kg (16¼ lb) with a 77-round drum magazine in place.

By the time the tests were completed, however, the postwar retrenchment had begun, and as a result the gun was not adopted for service although the design was sound. Had it appeared a couple of years earlier it is likely that it would have been adopted. The design was revived in 1940 and put forward once more, but by that time a gun firing at 450 rds/min was not good enough in the aircraft role and the suggestion was turned down.

Calibre: .303 in (7.7 mm) *Length:* 130 cm (50 in) approx *Weight:* 7.4 kg (16¼ lb) *Barrel:* 56 cm (26 in) approx *Magazine:* 77 rounds *Cyclic rate of fire:* 450 rds/min

Béarn

French aircraft carrier. In 1914 a battleship to be named *Vendée* was laid down at the Forges et Chantiers de la Méditerranée, La Seyne, Toulon shipyard. She was the fifth unit of the *Normandie* Class ordered under the Naval Law of March 30, 1912, but her name was soon changed to *Béarn*.

As most of the shipyard workers were to be conscripted into the army, work was suspended on the ship in 1915, when the hull was less than 25% complete. Work started

Taken aboard the *Béarn* in the early 1930s, this sequence of photographs shows a Levasseur PL 2 torpedo carrier being brought up to the flight deck—note the armoured flaps over the elevator—a PL 7 being manhandled into position and a PL 2 taking off

again in December 1918 but only to allow the hull to be launched; the future of the *Normandie* Class was under review, and in any case the boilers earmarked for them had been allocated to torpedo boats and escorts.

Following the Washington Conference in 1921-22 the French government authorized the conversion of the *Béarn* to an aircraft carrier. Work started on August 4, 1923 and the ship was ready in May 1927, but in 1921-22 tests had been carried out with aircraft landing on her incomplete main deck. She

Beaufighter, Bristol

was given a single hangar 124 m (406 ft 9 in) long, with three lifts connecting it to a flight deck 180 m (590 ft 9 in) long. The design of the hangar closely followed that of HMS *Eagle*, as the British Admiralty provided considerable technical advice, but unlike any other carrier, the *Béarn*'s lifts were protected by hinged armoured flaps.

The weakest point of the *Béarn*'s design was her slow speed of $21\frac{1}{2}$ knots, which hampered aircraft operations and made it impossible for her to operate with cruisers and, later, the battlecruisers *Dunkerque* and *Strasbourg*. The early French Zoelly turbines had proved highly uneconomical, and so when the *Normandie* Class was designed they were given turbines on the inner shafts only, and reciprocating engines on the outer shafts for cruising. The *Béarn* was originally intended to have an all-turbine installation, but finally she was given the engines from the *Normandie*.

In September 1939 the *Béarn*'s air group consisted of three dive-bomber squadrons, AB 1-3, formerly equipped with Loire Nieuport 41 dive-bombers but about to change to Chance Vought 156Fs. The three squadrons formed Flotille FIA, but as the ship was immediately earmarked to transport aircraft from the US the air group was sent to the Lanveoc-Poulnic shore/air station near Brest. These squadrons performed heroically during the German attack through Belgium and Holland.

Despite her lack of speed, the *Béarn* was attached to Force 'L', a group comprising the battlecruiser *Dunkerque* and three 6-in-gunned cruisers hunting for the *Admiral Graf Spee* out of Brest.

Shortly before the fall of France she was sent to Martinique in the West Indies, and on May 1, 1942 she was officially disarmed by the Governor to comply with the wishes of the United States. There she lay until the resignation of the Governor on June 30, 1943, when German forces entered the unoccupied half of France to seize the Toulon fleet. The ship went to the United States for a refit, but it was decided that her speed was too slow for her to be anything but a 'ferry carrier' or aircraft transport. In this role she served successfully until the end of the war in Europe and then took aircraft out to Indo-China for the war against the Viet-Minh until 1946. She was used for training in 1947-48.

As an aircraft transport she was considerably altered. The 155-mm guns in casemates forward and aft were removed and the flight deck overhang forward and aft was removed. The 5-in guns were mounted in open sponsons built in place of the casemates and a platform for light AA guns was built above the forecastle.

In her final years the *Béarn* was laid up at Toulon as an accommodation ship for submarines. She was put on the disposal list in 1966 and partially stripped at Toulon; the bare hull was towed to Italy for scrapping at the end of March 1967.

See also *Normandie* Class.

Displacement: 22 146 tons (standard), 25 000 tons (full load) *Length:* 182.6 m (599 ft 0 in) oa *Beam:* 27.13 m (89 ft 0 in) hull, 35.2 m (115 ft 6 in) across flight deck *Draught:* 9.3 m (30 ft 6 in) *Machinery:* 4-shaft steam turbine/reciprocating, 22 500 shp/15 000 ihp=$21\frac{1}{2}$ knots *Protection:* 83

Above: An aircraft, seen from the hangar deck, lands on the *Béarn. Below: Béarn*, converted *Normandie* Class battleship, at anchor

mm ($3\frac{1}{4}$ in) belt, 25 mm (1 in) flight and main decks, 70 mm ($2\frac{3}{4}$ in) lower deck, 64 mm ($2\frac{1}{2}$ in) gun positions *Armament:* (As completed) 8 155-mm (6.1-in)/55 cal (8×1); 6 75-mm (3-in) AA (6×1); 6 55-cm (21.7-in) torpedo tubes (submerged, broadside); 40 aircraft; (As refitted 1944) 4 127-mm (5-in)/38 cal DP (4×1); 24 40-mm AA (6×4); 26 20-mm AA (26×1) *Crew:* 875, reduced to 651 in 1944

Beast NATO code name for the Il-10 attack aircraft   See **Sturmovik**

Beaufighter, Bristol

British night fighter, attack aircraft and torpedo bomber. During the years 1935-39 the Air Staff and British industry made progress in circles trying to resolve the question of fighters having such features as long range, two engines or cannon armament. For three years, arguments raged over whether the armament should be fixed or carried in a power-driven turret, and eventually the chief designers of the Bristol aircraft and engine teams, respectively Leslie G Frise and A H Roy Fedden, decided during the Munich crisis in September 1938 that something had to be done quickly about providing a big, two-engined long-range fighter.

They prepared a brochure describing a fighter incorporating the wings and tail of the Beaufort, then just about to fly, but with more powerful 1375-hp Bristol Hercules sleeve-valve engines driving larger-diameter DH Hydromatic propellers, and with a new fuselage accommodating a crew of two. In March 1939 the turret was at last dropped and

Beaufighter Mk 1 in flight. Inset: Armourers fuz

rockets on an RAF Coastal Command Beaufighter immediately before takeoff on a strike against shipping in the North Sea

Flight International/Inset: MOD

Beaufort, Bristol

replaced by four 20-mm Hispano cannon in the underside of the nose. In the same month the Bristol project was named Beaufighter, and in July 1939, the month the prototype flew (on the 17th), the specification F.17/39 was written around it.

It was a big and heavy machine, and was found to lack both speed and manoeuvrability (speed barely exceeded 480 km/h, [300 mph]), and by June 1940, when the first Mk I aircraft reached the RAF to begin trials, the need seemed to be for small day interceptors. But, fortunately, large orders had been placed and the Beaufighter proved—almost entirely by chance, because the subject was never mentioned in any official specification—to be ideal as a carrier of the rapidly developing AI (airborne interception) radar.

First squadron deliveries were made to No 25 and No 29 Squadrons in July 1940, without radar, but from early September AI.IV was progressively installed, and crews gradually learned the difficult art of night interceptions. Only one or two scattered successes were gained during the 'night Blitz' on southern England from October 1940 until February 1941. Then kills mounted rapidly, 96 Luftwaffe bombers being destroyed in the final two weeks in May 1941—almost all of them by Beaufighters. By this time all 'Beaus' had a total of six .303-in Browning machine-guns in the outer wings, two on the left and four on the right, as well as the cannon, making it the most heavily armed aircraft of its day. From the start Bristol had designed a belt feed for the cannon, but due to official bungling this was not accepted until the 401st aircraft, in September 1941.

Owing to shortage of the higher-power versions of the Hercules engine, 450 early deliveries were fitted with the liquid-cooled Merlin. This gave similar speed but poorer climb and accentuated the tendency of the Beaufighter to 'hunt' longitudinally and in yaw; with inexperienced pilots, swing on takeoff and landing was also serious. During 1941 the position was improved by the introduction of more powerful Hercules VI and XVI engines rated at 1595 hp, a tailplane with dihedral and a long dorsal fin. These improve-

ments resulted in the VIC for Coastal Command and VIF for Fighter Command. Most Coastal aircraft, and the large numbers sent to the North African and Mediterranean theatres, had long-range tanks in the outer wings in place of the machine-guns. The observer in these versions was often armed with a Vickers K manually-aimed machine-gun, this member of the crew being responsible for navigation and, in the early nightfighter marks, for working the radar and reloading the cannon.

The Mks IF and VIF served in considerable numbers with the RAF and USAAF in the Mediterranean and throughout the Italian campaign as the standard US Army night fighter until arrival of the Black Widow in June 1944. Beaufighters flew on all fronts in the Second World War, and were especially important in Burma and Southeast Asia where they were known to the Japanese as 'Whispering Death' on account of their quiet Hercules engines and devastating firepower.

In May 1942 the first Beaufighter flew with a torpedo, and the final 2205 of the British total of 5564 were TF.X with torpedo and many other changes, including special Youngman bellows-type airbrakes incorporated in the flaps. A further 364 Mk 21 were built in Australia in 1944-45, with 12.7-mm wing guns and Sperry autopilot in a bulged nose. A Beaufighter was, in 1942, the first fighter in the world to fly with centimetric radar, in a 'thimble' nose radome, and both AI Mk VIII, and ASV radars flew in later types of Beaufighter. After 1945 many 'Beaus' were converted into TT.10 target tugs, while small numbers were exported to Turkey, Dominica and Portugal.

There were many non-standard Beaufighters, including examples with Griffon and Cyclone R-2600 engines, twin 40-mm cannon, dorsal turrets and twin fins. Examples are preserved in Britain, Australia and Canada.

Span: 17.63 m (57 ft 10 in) *Length:* (typical, without nose radar) 12.6 m (41 ft 8 in) *Gross weight:* (Mk X) 11530 kg (25400 lb) *Maximum speed:* (Mk X) 530 km/h (312 mph) (fighters, about 528 km/h, 330 mph)

Beaufort, Bristol

British torpedo bomber. Planned as a second-generation development of the Bristol 142 (the Blenheim being the first), this aircraft was a tremendous advance over the biplane Vildebeest which it replaced progressively from January 1940.

Unfortunately the Air Staff specifications M.15/35 and G.24/35 and (for the production machine) 10/36, were responsible for imposing severe handicaps, especially in suggesting engines of inadequate power (the Perseus) and a crew of four. Compared with the Blenheim, the Bristol 152 was designed to have a deeper fuselage, though the torpedo was still carried semi-externally. After much development the engines chosen were two of the relatively undeveloped Bristol Taurus 14-cylinder sleeve-valve radials initially rated at 1065 hp and attractive because of their extremely compact form and small diameter.

The prototype 152, by this time named Beaufort, flew on October 15, 1938. After many changes the Beaufort I was cleared for service in November 1939, with twin .303-in Vickers K guns in a Daimler dorsal turret, one remotely-aimed .303-in Browning in a blister firing aft under the nose and various arrangements of from one to four Brownings fixed to fire ahead. Engines were 1130-hp Taurus VI, but reliability was poor and accidents due to engine failure frequent.

Action opened with the mining of the Jade Estuary on April 15/16, 1940, followed soon after by an attack with 907-kg (2000-lb) armour-piercing bombs on surface ships. By 1940 a special government organization had been set up in Australia to make a modified version with Pratt & Whitney Twin Wasp R-1830 engines, and the same American engine was used in 165 British-built Beauforts, plus 250 built later as trainers, all designated Mk II. But the main combat type remained the Mk I, which made gallant attacks from the Shetlands to Egypt and among many other achievements scored a direct hit on *Gneisenau* on April 6, 1941 (the No 22 Squadron skipper, F/O K Campbell, being awarded a posthumous VC).

The large and powerful Beaufighter Mk 1 proved—almost by accident—to be an ideal vehicle for early airborne interception radar sets

Total Mk I production, all by Bristol, was 1014. Australian production amounted to 700, Mks V to VIII progressively introducing a broader vertical tail, Australian-built R-1830 engines, ASV radar and other advances. These aircraft operated with daring and increasing success throughout the Southwest

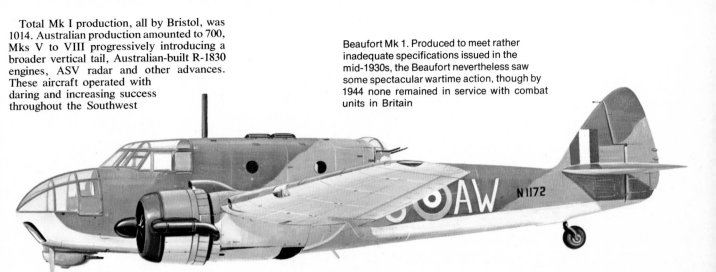

Beaufort Mk 1. Produced to meet rather inadequate specifications issued in the mid-1930s, the Beaufort nevertheless saw some spectacular wartime action, though by 1944 none remained in service with combat units in Britain

Pacific area from mid-1942 until VJ-Day. A batch of 46 Mk VIII were converted as transports, designated Beaufort IX. Total output amounted to 2080.

That the original specification was faulty is shown by the fact that the Beaufighter, with only two seats and much higher performance, began to replace the Beaufort as early as November 1942, and by 1944 no Beauforts remained in combat units in Britain. Six Mk I aircraft were supplied to Turkey in 1939-40. No Beaufort exists today.

Span: 17.63 m (57 ft 10 in) *Length:* 13.46 m (44 ft 2 in) (some marks, 44 ft 7 in) *Gross weight:* (I) 9629 kg (21 230 lb), (II, VIII) 10 206 kg (22 500 lb) *Maximum speed:* (I, without torpedo) 418 km/h (260 mph), (II, VIII) 370 km/h (230 mph)

Beeswing British antitank missile
See **Swingfire**

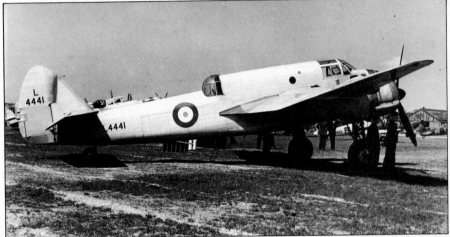

An early Beaufort Mk 1 forms part of a display of RAF aircraft at Northolt, May 1939

Flight International

The 7.65-mm Beholla German automatic pistol, a robust blowback weapon adopted by the German army in 1915. Demand was so great that manufacture was undertaken by three other companies who produced it as the Stenda, Leonhardt and Menta

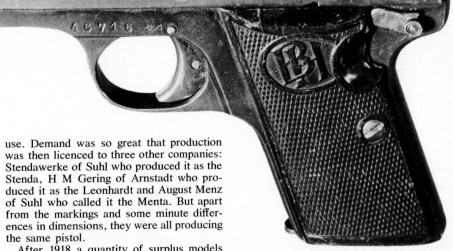

Beholla

German automatic pistol. Developed by Becker & Hollander of Suhl, from which the name was derived, this was a cheap, simple and robust blowback pistol in 7.65-mm Browning calibre. Its single notable mechanical feature was the fact that it could only be dismantled in a workshop and not in the field, since the barrel and slide were retained in place by a tight-fitting pin. It had a seven-shot magazine and was fired by means of an internal hammer.

The Beholla was originally intended for commercial sale and went into production early in 1915, but at that time the German army needed all the pistols it could get, and the entire production was taken for military use. Demand was so great that production was then licenced to three other companies: Stendawerke of Suhl who produced it as the Stenda, H M Gering of Arnstadt who produced it as the Leonhardt and August Menz of Suhl who called it the Menta. But apart from the markings and some minute differences in dimensions, they were all producing the same pistol.

After 1918 a quantity of surplus models

I V Hogg

Beholla

was sold commercially. Subsequently the Stenda company made some changes in the design, notably to improve the method of dismantling, and continued to market the Stenda until the mid-1920s.

Calibre: 7.65 mm *Length:* 14.0 cm (5.5 in) *Weight:* 630 g (22.3 oz) approx *Barrel:* 7.4 cm (2.9 in) *Magazine:* 7 rds

HMS *Edinburgh* (above and top) in late 1941 and *Belfast* (right) in February 1953. *Edinburgh*'s wartime career ended with her sinking in the spring of 1942, but *Belfast,* although mined in 1939, was refitted, serving out the war and later seeing action off Korea

Belfast

British cruiser class. Constructed under the 1937 Programme, the *Belfast* and *Edinburgh* were modified versions of the *Southampton* Class cruisers. As originally designed, they would have differed from the earlier ships in having four quadruple 6-in gun turrets instead of triples. This would have placed them on equal terms with contemporary US and Japanese cruisers. The heavier armament necessitated a larger hull, resulting in an increase in the displacement to 10 000 tons. However, trials with the prototype quad 6-in mounting were not successful, and after considering the difficulties and delays involved in designing a satisfactory alternative it was decided to abandon the quad mounting and revert to the triple turrets of the earlier *Southampton* Class cruisers.

The design was modified accordingly, and as finally worked out they differed from the *Southampton* mainly in appearance. This was the result of moving the 4-in magazines from abaft the machinery to forward of it, which in turn necessitated moving the machinery further aft. Consequently there was a substantial increase in the distance between the fore funnel and the bridge. Other differences were less obvious, the most important being a general improvement in the armour protection, both in thickness and distribution, and an increase of the armament by the fitting of two more twin 4-in gun mountings.

Ordered and laid down in 1936, both vessels were launched in 1938 and completed in the following year. The *Edinburgh* was constructed by Swan Hunter on the Tyne and the *Belfast* by Harland and Wolff at Belfast.

The *Edinburgh*'s career was comparatively short. On April 30, 1942, while escorting the Russian convoy QP11, she was torpedoed by the *U 456*. Despite heavy damage she eventually worked up speed to 8 knots and headed for Kola Inlet, but two days later she was intercepted by a group of German destroyers off Bear Island. In the engagement which followed she was torpedoed again, and all chance of saving her having been lost, she was abandoned and subsequently sunk by a torpedo from the destroyer *Foresight*.

The *Belfast* came close to having an even shorter career. On November 21, 1939 she detonated a magnetic mine in the Firth of Forth. The resulting damage was extensive—the keel was broken, the hull distorted and strained, the machinery suffered severe shock damage and the centre section of the ship was flooded. Later in the war she would have been written off as a total loss, but after temporary repairs at Rosyth she was taken to Devonport for a two-year repair and refit which was completed in October 1942. The hull was straightened and, to strengthen the damaged portion of the ship and improve stability, a narrow bulge was added on each side increasing the beam to 21 m (69 ft). At the same time the 0.5-in guns were removed and 14 20-mm (5×2+4×1) guns added, together with the standard radar equipment of the time. By 1944 a further 12 20-mm (10×1+1×2) guns had been added.

She recommissioned in November 1942 and spent a large part of the next 18 months covering Russian convoys. During one of these operations, on December 26, 1942, she took part in the Battle of North Cape in

MOD

305

Belknap

which the battlecruiser *Scharnhorst* was sunk by the battleship *Duke of York* and other units of the Home Fleet. After serving as a bombardment ship during the invasion of Normandy she was taken in hand for a refit for service in the Pacific. Modifications included the removal of the aircraft equipment, two of her twin 4-in mountings and eight 20-mm (8×1) and the addition of 20 2-pdr pom-poms (4×4+4×1).

She arrived at Sydney in August 1945 where five 40-mm (5×1) guns were added to the armament and four 20-mm (2×2) removed. The war with Japan ended before she could become involved, but she spent the major part of the next eight years in the Far East and took an active part in the Korean war during 1950-52.

In 1953 she was placed in reserve and between 1956 and 1959 was extensively modernized at Devonport. Alterations included a new bridge, lattice masts, substitution of 12 40-mm (6×2) guns for the existing close-range armament, a substantial improvement in her fire control, radar and communication equipment and the removal of the torpedo tubes. On completion of this refit her displacement had risen to 11 550 tons standard and 14 930 tons full load. This made her Britain's largest 6-in-gun cruiser, but claims that she is the largest ever British cruiser are exaggerated. Some of Britain's 8-in-gun cruisers exceeded the full load of *Belfast* during the Second World War and certain 1st Class cruisers built around the turn of the century were also larger.

Despite the expensive modernization she served only four years before being placed in reserve and was subsequently listed for disposal. However, after a difficult battle to save her from the breakers the government agreed in 1971 to place the ship under the control of the HMS *Belfast* Trust. She now serves as a museum ship, being permanently moored in the Pool of London.

See also *Southampton* Class.

Displacement: 10 550 tons (standard) *Length:* 187 m (613 ft 6 in) oa *Beam:* 19.3 m (63 ft 4 in) *Draught:* 5.26 m (17 ft 3 in) *Machinery:* 4-shaft geared steam turbines, 80 000 shp=32.5 knots *Protection:* 114 mm (4½ in) side; 51-102 mm (2-4 in) turrets; 51-76 mm (2-3 in) decks *Armament:* 12 6-in (152-mm) (4×3); 12 4-in (102-mm) (6×2); 16 2-pdr (2×8); 8 0.5-in (12.7-mm) (2×4); 6 21-in (53-cm) torpedo tubes (2×3, above water) *Aircraft:* 2 *Crew:* 880

Belknap

US guided missile cruiser class. Three guided missile destroyers (DLG.26-28) were authorized for the US Navy in the Fiscal Year 1961 building programme, followed by DLG.29-34 in the FY 1962 programme, and they were built between 1962 and 1967.

The *Belknaps* are improved versions of the 'double-ended' *Leahy* Class DLGs, to which they have a general resemblance. But in this class there is only one missile launcher forward and a 5-in gun mounting aft. The reason for this is that more missiles can be stowed in the broader forward section of the hull and allow space aft for a helicopter hangar. The added space is needed as the launcher fires both Terrier (since replaced by Standard) and Asroc missiles, and the inclusion of the 5-in

HMS *Belfast* during bombardments of enemy troop concentrations off the west coast of Korea

gun mounting is the result of experience in Vietnam when shore bombardments were in frequent demand.

The dual-purpose Standard/Asroc launcher is a Mk 10 Mod 7, with a triple-ring rotating magazine capable of supplying either type of missile to either arm of the launcher. Two Mk 76 Mod 4 control systems are provided for air defence and the 5-in gun is controlled by a Mk 68 Mod 8 fire control system. The two single 3-in guns at the after end of the forecastle deck are controlled by Mk 51 and Mod 3 systems. When the ships were first commissioned they had two 21-in torpedo

tubes for antisubmarine torpedoes installed at the break of the forecastle, angled out, but these were later removed.

The sonar is a bow-mounted SQS-26 set, linked to the Asroc system and the triple Mk 32 torpedo tubes amidships. Aerials for the SPS-48 3-D and SPS-10 search radars are mounted on the forward 'mack', while the array for SPS-37 (in DLG.26-28) or SPS-40 search radar is on the after 'mack' with a small tactical aircraft navigation (TACAN) aerial. The Mk 11 Mod 0 weapon direction system is installed, with SPG-53A and SPG-55B weapon control radars.

Number	name	laid down	launched	completed	built
CG.26 (ex-DLG.26)	*Belknap*	2/1962	7/1963	11/1964	Bath Iron Works, Maine
CG.27 (ex-DLG.27)	*Josephus Daniels*	4/1962	12/1963	5/1965	Bath Iron Works, Maine
CG.28 (ex-DLG.28)	*Wainwright*	7/1962	4/1964	1/1966	Bath Iron Works, Maine
CG.29 (ex-DLG.29)	*Jouett*	9/1962	6/1964	12/1966	Puget Sound Naval Shipyard
CG.30 (ex-DLG.30)	*Horne*	12/1962	10/1964	4/1967	San Francisco Naval Shipyard
CG.31 (ex-DLG.31)	*Sterett*	9/1962	6/1964	4/1967	Puget Sound Naval Shipyard
CG.32 (ex-DLG.32)	*William H Stanley*	7/1963	12/1964	7/1966	Bath Iron Works, Maine
CG.33 (ex-DLG.33)	*Fox*	1/1963	11/1964	5/1966	Todd Shipyard Corporation
CG.34 (ex-DLG.34)	*Biddle*	12/1963	7/1965	1/1967	Bath Iron Works, Maine

US Navy

The guided missile cruiser USS *Belknap* (CG.26). The Asroc/Terrier launcher is positioned forward, and is seen here loaded with two Terriers

Bellanca 28-110

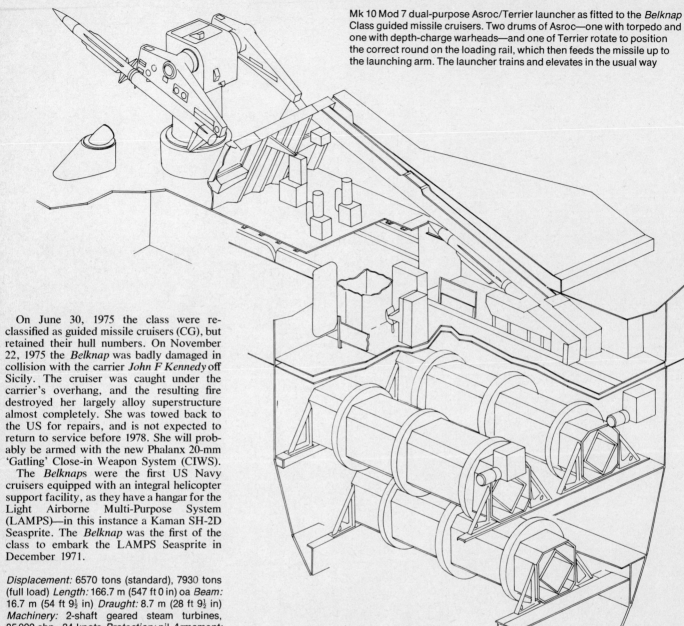

Mk 10 Mod 7 dual-purpose Asroc/Terrier launcher as fitted to the *Belknap* Class guided missile cruisers. Two drums of Asroc—one with torpedo and one with depth-charge warheads—and one of Terrier rotate to position the correct round on the loading rail, which then feeds the missile up to the launching arm. The launcher trains and elevates in the usual way

On June 30, 1975 the class were reclassified as guided missile cruisers (CG), but retained their hull numbers. On November 22, 1975 the *Belknap* was badly damaged in collision with the carrier *John F Kennedy* off Sicily. The cruiser was caught under the carrier's overhang, and the resulting fire destroyed her largely alloy superstructure almost completely. She was towed back to the US for repairs, and is not expected to return to service before 1978. She will probably be armed with the new Phalanx 20-mm 'Gatling' Close-in Weapon System (CIWS).

The *Belknap*s were the first US Navy cruisers equipped with an integral helicopter support facility, as they have a hangar for the Light Airborne Multi-Purpose System (LAMPS)—in this instance a Kaman SH-2D Seasprite. The *Belknap* was the first of the class to embark the LAMPS Seasprite in December 1971.

Displacement: 6570 tons (standard), 7930 tons (full load) *Length:* 166.7 m (547 ft 0 in) oa *Beam:* 16.7 m (54 ft 9½ in) *Draught:* 8.7 m (28 ft 9½ in) *Machinery:* 2-shaft geared steam turbines, 85 000 shp=34 knots *Protection:* nil *Armament:* 1 twin Terrier RIM-2/Asroc RUR-5A combined surface-to-air/surface-to-subsurface guided weapon systems (Terrier replaced by Standard ER RIM-67A); 1 5-in (127-mm)/54-cal Mk 42; 2 3-in (76-mm)/50-cal Mk 34 (2 × 1); 2 triple 12.75-in (32.4-cm) Mk 32 torpedo tubes for Mk 44/46 A/S torpedoes; 2 21-in (53-cm) torpedo tubes (removed) *Aircraft:* 1 SH-2D Seasprite helicopter *Crew:* 418 (436 as flagships)

Bellanca 28-110

American attack aircraft. In 1934 Bellanca Aircraft delivered to Col Fitzmaurice a special racer for the race from Mildenhall (UK) to Melbourne. From this streamlined monoplane, with a Twin Wasp engine and retractable landing gear, came several offshoots.

The 28-90 was ordered as a batch of 20 mailplanes for France, with 900-hp Twin Wasp engines, taken over by the Spanish Republicans and barred from export by the US government in 1938. Next, the Chinese ordered a heavily armed 'fighter' designated

28-110, with 1000-hp Twin Wasp, five machine-guns, a bombload of 726 kg (1600 lb) and full combat equipment. The first 20 are believed to have been modified from the impounded 28-90 batch, but little was heard of their performance in China.

Span: 14.1 m (46 ft 2 in) *Length:* 8.08 m (26 ft 6 in) *Gross weight:* 3560 kg (7849 lb) *Maximum speed:* 450 km/h (280 mph)

Bellanca 77-140

American bomber and transport. Though it achieved fame with several families of high-performance racing and transport aircraft, as well as lightplanes (in which field there are now two Bellanca companies), the original firm achieved only sporadic sales of military machines. Colombia was a purchaser of a small batch of 77-140 bomber versions of the Airbus transport of 1935.

A typical robust steel-tube product of Bellanca Aircraft Corporation, this model had two 715-hp Wright Cyclone G-series engines on its high wing and was available with spatted wheels or twin floats. Five machine-guns were carried in five separate locations (bow, each side at rear, and above and below at rear), and with a long-range tank in the fuselage it was possible to fly 2415 km (1500 miles) with the full bombload of 907 kg (2000 lb). A prominent feature of these and the widely used single-engined Aircruisers was a wing bracing strut that was actually a slim tapering wing.

Span: 23.16 m (76 ft 0 in) *Length:* (landplane) 12.19 m (40 ft 0 in), (seaplane) 13.75 m (45 ft 2 in) *Gross weight:* (landplane) 7410 kg (16 333 lb), (seaplane) 8050 kg (17 749 lb) *Maximum speed:* (landplane) 306 km/h (190 mph), (seaplane) 282 km/h (175 mph)

National Maritime Museum

Bellerophon

British battleship class. Having revolutionized battleship design with the construction of the *Dreadnought*, the Admiralty prepared a programme for the laying-down of three *Dreadnought*-type battleships per year. This, it was considered, would be a sufficient number to allow the Royal Navy to retain its position of supremacy among the world's battle fleets.

The first of these vessels were the three ships of the *Bellerophon* Class, constructed under the 1906-07 Programme. They were virtually repeat editions of the *Dreadnought* with a few improvements and some rearrangement of detail. The principal changes were the substitution of 4-in for 12-pdr (3-in) guns in the secondary battery, the fitting of internal torpedo bulkheads over the full length of magazine and machinery spaces and an increase in the thickness of the main deck. The general layout remained the same as the *Dreadnought*'s except that the foremast was stepped forward of instead of abaft the forefunnel, thus avoiding the possibility of funnel gases interfering with the operations of the foretop. All these alterations necessitated the addition of a considerable amount of weight, and by way of compensation the barbette and belt armour were reduced in thickness and the fuel capacity cut down. However, the ships were slightly larger than *Dreadnought*, with 700 tons added to the displacement and 6 in to the beam.

The *Bellerophon* was laid down in 1906 and her sisters in 1907; all were launched in 1907 and completed in 1909. They served in the 1st Division of the Home Fleet until May 1912 when they became part of the 1st Battle Squadron. On the outbreak of war Bel-

Bellerophon (below) as completed, and her sister *Temeraire* (above) in 1918, with 4-in guns removed from the turrets, new control top and AA gun on the after searchlight platform

Real Photographs

lerophon and *Temeraire* joined the 4th Battle Squadron of the Grand Fleet, but *Superb* remained with the 1st Squadron until 1915 when she also joined the 4th. All three took part in the Battle of Jutland. In 1918 *Temeraire* and *Superb* transferred to the Mediterranean, where the latter vessel led the Allied Fleet through the Dardanelles after the surrender of Turkey.

War modifications were fairly standard and included the fitting of gun directors, searchlight towers, aircraft flying-off platforms, two antiaircraft guns, the removal of the stern torpedo tube and the transfer of 4-in guns from turret tops to the superstructure. The *Bellerophon* was sold for scrap in November

1921 and the *Temeraire* and *Superb* in December 1922.

Bellerophon—built by Portsmouth dockyard
Temeraire—built by Devonport dockyard
Superb—built by Armstrong at Elswick

Displacement: 18 800 tons *Length:* 160.32 m (526 ft) oa *Beam:* 25.15 m (82 ft 6 in) *Draught:* 8.23 m (27 ft) *Machinery:* 4-shaft steam turbines, 23 000 shp=22 knots *Protection:* 10 in (254 mm) belt; 9 in (229 mm) barbettes; $\frac{3}{4}$-1$\frac{3}{4}$ in (19-45 mm) decks; 1-2 in (25-50 mm) torpedo bulkheads *Armament:* 10 12-in (305-mm) (5×2); 16 4-in (102-mm) (16×1); 3 21-in (53-cm) torpedo tubes (3×1 submerged, 2 broadside, 1 stern) *Crew:* 780

Belmont

Belmont

British destroyer class. The *Belmont* Class of 20 ships formed the fourth and final group of old destroyers—collectively known as the 'Town' Classes—supplied to the Royal Navy by the United States under lend-lease. All this group were originally members of the American *Clemson* Class, the third class of the famous flush-deck destroyers designed during the First World War with flush decks for rapid building. Built to two basic designs, one by Bethlehem Steel and one by Bath Iron Works, they were launched between 1918 and 1920 by various yards, the first seven by Newport News and the remaining 13

by Bethlehem at Quincy and Squantum.

Transferred to the Royal Navy in 1940 to help meet the desperate need for convoy escorts, they were all modified to reduce topweight, and those that survived into 1942 were extensively modified for the escort role. The 4-in guns amidships were removed, being replaced by single 20-mm AA, while a British 12-pdr replaced the after 4-in. Only one triple bank of torpedo tubes was retained, for firing Mk 10 depth charges, a twin 20-mm being added, and the other A/S weapons included a Hedgehog on the forecastle and four depth-charge mortars and two racks on the stern.

The *Belmont*s suffered heavily during the war, six vessels being sunk by U-Boats alone.

RN name	US name & number
Belmont	*Satterlee* DD.190
Beverley	*Branch* DD.197
Broadwater	*Mason* DD.191
Broadway	*Hunt* DD.194
Chesterfield	*Welborn C Wood* DD.195
Churchill	*Herndon* DD.198
Clare	*Abel P Upshur* DD.193
Bradford	*McLanahan* DD.264
Burnham	*Aulick* DD.258
Burwell	*Laub* DD.263
Buxton	*Edwards* DD.265
Cameron	*Welles* DD.257
Ramsey	*Meade* DD.274
Reading	*Bailey* DD.269
Ripley	*Shubrick* DD.268
Rockingham	*Swasey* DD.273
St Croix	*McCook* DD.252
St Francis	*Bancroft* DD.256
Sherwood	*Rodgers* DD.254
Stanley	*McCalla* DD.253

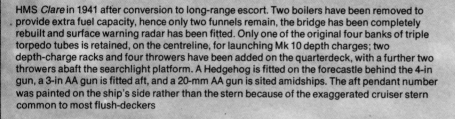

HMS *Clare* in 1941 after conversion to long-range escort. Two boilers have been removed to provide extra fuel capacity, hence only two funnels remain, the bridge has been completely rebuilt and surface warning radar has been fitted. Only one of the original four banks of triple torpedo tubes is retained, on the centreline, for launching Mk 10 depth charges; two depth-charge racks and four throwers have been added on the quarterdeck, with a further two throwers abaft the searchlight platform. A Hedgehog is fitted on the forecastle behind the 4-in gun, a 3-in AA gun is fitted aft, and a 20-mm AA gun is sited amidships. The aft pendant number was painted on the ship's side rather than the stern because of the exaggerated cruiser stern common to most flush-deckers

First casualty was *Cameron*, bombed at Portsmouth in December 1940 and hulked. *Broadwater* was sunk by *U 101* south of Ireland on October 18, 1941, and on December 19 *Stanley* was sunk by *U 574* southwest of Portugal. Six weeks later, on January 31, 1942, the *Belmont* herself was sunk by *U 82* off Halifax, Nova Scotia. *Beverley* was sunk south of Greenland by *U 188* in April 1943; *St Croix* was torpedoed and sunk south of Ireland by *U 305* in September 1943. The *Rockingham* was mined off Aberdeen on September 27, 1944. *Churchill* served with the Russian navy as the *Deiatelnyi* in 1944-45, finally being sunk in the Arctic by *U 596* on January 1, 1945.

The remainder of the class survived the war and were sold for scrapping during the three years after its end, except for *St Francis*, which was lost on passage to the shipbreakers on July 14, 1945.

Displacement: 1190 tons (standard) *Length:* 95.85 m (314 ft 6 in) oa *Beam:* 9.68 m (31 ft 9 in) *Draught:* 2.82 m (9 ft 3 in) *Machinery:* 2-shaft geared turbines, 26 000 shp=35 knots *Armament:* (As built) 4 4-in (102-mm); 1 3-in (76-mm) AA; 3 0.5-in AA; 12 21-in (53-cm) torpedo tubes (4×3); (As initially modified) 3 4-in; 1 3-in; 4/5 20-mm AA; 3 21-in torpedo tubes; 1 Hedgehog antisubmarine weapon (Further modifications carried out as required) *Crew:* 146

Beluga

French grenade-dispensing bomb. Developed jointly by Engins Matra and Thomson Brandt, Beluga is a dispersion weapon which enables stationary or moving targets to be attacked by strike aircraft flying at high speed and low level. It consists of a canister containing 151 grenades of 66-mm (2.59-in) calibre, each weighing 1.2 kg (2.64 lb). The canister fits standard NATO 14-in (35.5-cm) lugs and can withstand high g-loads and supersonic speed during carriage. Release can take place at heights down to 60 m (197 ft) and at speeds up to 540 knots.

After release the bomb is braked before

PPL

sequential ejection of the grenades, which are themselves retarded and descend almost vertically. Three types of grenade have been developed for use with Beluga: a small general-purpose fragmentation bomb for use against vehicles, parked aircraft and equipment and fuel stores; an armour-piercing version for attacking tanks and other armoured vehicles; and an area-interdiction variant effective against airfields, harbours, marshalling yards and road junctions. The cloud of grenades covers a strip 40-60 m (44-66 yards) wide, and the pilot can select a strip length of either 120 m (393 ft) or 240 m (787 ft) before release.

Beluga has been designed to carry the maximum number of grenades within a low-drag canister and is supplied as a complete 'round of ammunition' in a special packing. The braking action of the bomb itself ensures that the launch aircraft—typically a Jaguar fighter-bomber—is well clear of the weapon when the grenades are ejected. Beluga's effectiveness is classified but is likely to be very similar to that of Britain's Hunting Engineering BL755 cluster bomb.

Span: 58 cm (22.8 in) *Length:* 330 cm (10 ft) *Weight:* 290 kg (640 lb)

Beluga

Russian submarine class. Five Holland-type submarines were ordered from the Electric Boat company in 1904, and were delivered to the Russian Baltic Fleet in 1905-06. One of them had been built on speculation by the Electric Boat company as the *Fulton.* Despite their age they were still operational when war broke out in 1914. On May 20, 1916 the *Som* was one of a number of submarines which made a sortie against German shipping in the Gulf of Bothnia, but on May 23 she was sunk in a collision with the Swedish steamer *Angermanland* in the Aaland Strait. Three others were at Libau in August 1914, among them the *Sterlad*, and were attached to the submarine school.

Most of the old submarines, including the four Holland boats, were taken out of service at the end of November 1916 to provide crews for the new 'AG' Class and others. They were scrapped after the Revolution.

Displacement: 103/124 tons (surfaced/submerged) *Length:* 19.3 m (63 ft 4 in) pp *Beam:* 3.6 m (11 ft 10 in) *Draught:* 3.1 m (10 ft 2 in) *Machinery:* Gasoline motor/electric motor, 160 bhp/170 hp=8/6.3 knots (surfaced/submerged)

Armament: 1 18-in (46-cm) torpedo tube; 1 37-mm gun added during 1915 *Crew:* 14

Name	completed
Beluga	1905
Peskar	1905
Schuka	1905
Som (ex-*Fulton*)	4/1904
Sterlad	1906

Benham

US destroyer class. The 12 destroyers of this class were generally similar to the *Gridley* (DD.380) Class built in 1935-38, but had more fuel, slightly lower speed and one boiler less than those of the earlier class.

The class was designed for the Pacific, and to counter the heavy torpedo-armament of Japanese destroyers they were given 16 tubes in four quadruple mountings on the beam. To achieve this concentration of armament with-

Matra/Thomson Brandt Beluga 66-mm (2.59-in) grenade-dispensing bombs fitted under the wing of a SEPECAT Jaguar of the Armée de l'Air

out encroaching on deck space or increasing topweight too much, the boiler uptakes were trunked into a single funnel. This afforded the main distinction between the *Benham*s and the *Gridley*s; the *Benham*s had less prominent trunking and had a short bulwark extending from the break of the forecastle.

The class bore the brunt of the fighting in the Pacific in 1942 and performed well, but the addition of radar and AA guns showed that topweight would have to be reduced. Some ships had their after banks of torpedo tubes removed, for example *Lang*, and others had the two remaining banks resited on the centreline. In addition to single 20-mm Oerlikons (6 or 8) they were given two twin 40-mm Bofors gun-mountings at the forward end of the after deckhouse, and a much-needed shield was provided for Y 5-in gun, as it had previously proved almost unworkable in rough weather.

Benham was torpedoed by Japanese warships during the Battle of Guadalcanal at 2338 on the night of November 14, 1942, but at 0300 the following morning the *Gwin* took her in tow, making for Espiritu Santo. At 1500 that afternoon the *Benham*'s badly damaged bulkheads began to collapse, and after taking off the survivors the *Gwin* sank her with 5-in gunfire. Only seven men were wounded in the action, and Lieutenant-Commander John B Taylor was awarded the Navy Cross.

The *Rowan* was one of the few US warships sunk in the European theatre, being torpedoed by a German Schnellboot off Salerno on September 10, 1943. The survivors did not last long after the war. The *Lang* was sold in 1945 for scrapping and four others were sold in 1946-47. The *Mayrant*, *Trippe*, *Rhind*, *Stack* and *Wilson* were all used as targets at Bikini Atoll in July 1946, and, like so many other ships, became so radio-active as to be dangerous and consequently they had to be scuttled.

Displacement: 1500 tons (standard), 2350 tons (full load) *Length:* (DD.397, 398, 404, 408) 104 m (341 ft 3 in) oa; (DD.399, 402, 403, 407) 103.94 m (341 ft 0 in) oa; (DD.400, 401) 104.09 m (341 ft 6 in) oa; (DD.406) 103.88 m (340 ft 9 in) oa; (DD.405) 103.78 m (340 ft 6 in) oa *Beam:* 10.82 m (35 ft 6 in) *Draught:* 5.18 m (17 ft) full load *Machinery:* 2-shaft single-reduction geared steam turbines, 50 000 shp=36½ knots (smooth-water speed only) *Armament:* 4 5-in (127-mm)/38-cal DP (4×1); 4 .5-in AA machine-guns (4×1); 16 21-in (53-cm) torpedo tubes (4×4) *Crew:* 184

Benjamin Franklin

US ballistic-missile submarine class. The *Benjamin Franklin* Class of 12 nuclear submarines are repeats of the *Lafayette* (SSBN.616) Class built in 1961-64. Although they have the same hull their machinery was redesigned to reduce running noise, and other minor improvements were made. They were initially armed with the A-3 Polaris ballistic missile, but since 1970 they have been converted to fire the C-3 Poseidon missile; the last boat completed conversion in February 1974. All boats were fitted with snorkels.

The conversion to Poseidon involved the replacement of the Mk 84 fire-control system with the Mk 88. The Mk 113 Mod 9 torpedo fire-control system is also fitted. It is possible

Hull no and name	laid down	launched	completed	builder
DD.397 *Benham*	9/1936	4/1938	4/1939	Federal shipbuilders
DD.398 *Ellet*	12/1936	6/1938	4/1939	Federal shipbuilders
DD.399 *Lang*	4/1937	8/1938	5/1939	Federal shipbuilders
DD.400 *McCall*	3/1936	11/1937	12/1938	Bethlehem, San Francisco
DD.401 *Maury*	3/1936	2/1938	1/1939	Bethlehem, San Francisco
DD.402 *Mayrant*	4/1937	5/1938	11/1939	Boston navy yard
DD.403 *Trippe*	4/1937	5/1938	12/1939	Boston navy yard
DD.404 *Rhind*	9/1937	7/1938	1/1940	Philadelphia navy yard
DD.405 *Rowan*	6/1937	5/1938	10/1939	Norfolk navy yard
DD.406 *Stack*	6/1937	5/1938	1/1940	Norfolk navy yard
DD.407 *Sterrett*	12/1936	10/1938	9/1939	Charleston navy yard
DD.408 *Wilson*	3/1937	4/1939	8/1939	Bremerton navy yard

that some of the class may be armed with the Trident I missile to give longer range—4828-6437 km (3000-4000 miles)—than the Poseidon's 4630 km (2875 miles).

Displacement: 7250 tons/8250 tons (surfaced/submerged) *Length:* 129.5 m (425 ft) oa *Beam:* 10.1 m (33 ft) *Draught:* 9.6 m (31 ft 6 in) *Machinery:* Single-shaft twin-geared steam turbines, pressurized water-cooled S5W nuclear reactor, 15 000 shp=20/30 knots (surfaced/submerged)+diesel/electric emergency propulsion unit *Armament:* 16 C-3 Poseidon ballistic missiles; 4 21-in (53-cm) torpedo tubes (forward) *Crew:* 145

Ben-My-Chree

British seaplane carrier. The *Ben-My-Chree* was one of six cross-Channel ferries taken over by the Royal Navy in 1914 for conversion to seaplane carriers. These vessels were chosen because of their high speed and, at that time, the *Ben-My-Chree* was the fastest

Hull no and name	laid down	launched	completed	builder
SSBN.640 *Benjamin Franklin*	5/1963	12/1964	10/1965	General Dynamics
SSBN.641 *Simon Bolivar*	4/1963	8/1964	10/1965	Newport News shipbuilders
SSBN.642 *Kamehameha*	5/1963	1/1965	12/1965	Mare Island navy yard
SSBN.643 *George Bancroft*	8/1963	3/1965	1/1966	General Dynamics
SSBN.644 *Lewis and Clark*	7/1963	11/1964	12/1965	Newport News shipbuilders
SSBN.645 *James K Polk*	11/1963	5/1965	4/1966	General Dynamics
SSBN.654 *George C Marshall*	3/1964	5/1965	4/1966	Newport News shipbuilders
SSBN.655 *Henry L Stimson*	4/1964	11/1965	8/1966	General Dynamics
SSBN.656 *George Washington Carver*	8/1964	8/1965	6/1966	Newport News shipbuilders
SSBN.657 *Francis Scott Key*	12/1964	4/1966	12/1966	General Dynamics
SSBN.658 *Mariana G Vallejo*	7/1964	10/1965	12/1966	Mare Island navy yard
SSBN.659 *Will Rogers*	3/1965	7/1966	4/1967	General Dynamics

ship of her type in service. Launched in 1908, she belonged to the Isle of Man Steamship company and normally operated between Liverpool and the Isle of Man. Alterations to the ship, carried out by Cammell Laird at Birkenhead, were comparatively few, the most noticeable addition being the fitting of a large hangar for four aircraft over the after part of the superstructure. In addition, a flying-off platform (seldom, if ever, used) was added over the forecastle and a sampson post and derrick, for hoisting seaplanes in and out, was added on the quarterdeck. She was fitted with an armament of two 12-pdr guns on the forecastle and two 3-pdr AA on the hangar roof.

Ben-My-Chree commissioned on January 2, 1915 and, after a short spell in home waters, went out to the Eastern Mediterranean. The aircraft she carried were Short 184 seaplanes. Arriving on June 12, she remained there until 1916 and took part in the Gallipoli campaign. On August 12, 1915 a Short 184 from the *Ben-My-Chree* carried out the first successful aerial torpedo attack. However, the victim, a Turkish supply ship, was a sitting target, as it lay aground in the Dardanelles, having been torpedoed a few days earlier by a destroyer. On August 17 the operation was repeated, this time using two seaplanes. One torpedoed and seriously damaged another supply ship and the other sank a tug, although in this latter case the aircraft was taxiing on the surface when it released its torpedo. In October and November *Ben-My-Chree*'s aircraft were used to bomb the Berlin-Constantinople railway link, but little could be done to much effect with their tiny 50.8-kg (112-lb) bombs.

In January 1916 *Ben-My-Chree* was trans-ferred to the command of the C-in-C East Indies for operations in the Red Sea area. During that year her aircraft were in action against the Turkish army in Palestine, the Sinai Peninsula and the Yemen, and for a short period she returned to the Aegean to operate against Bulgarian forces. On January 8, 1917 she was hit and set on fire by Turkish shore batteries off Castelorizo on the southern coast of Asia Minor. She burned for another two days and finally sank at her moorings. The wreck was raised by the Ocean Salvage company in 1920 and scrapped in Italy.

Displacement: 3888 tons (normal) *Length:* 119.35 m (387 ft) oa *Beam:* 14.19 m (46 ft) *Draught:* 4.63 m (15 ft) *Machinery:* 3-shaft steam turbines, 14000 shp=24.5 knots *Armament:* 2 12-pdr (2×1); 2 3-pdr AA (2×1) *Aircraft:* 6 (2 carried as spare airframes only) *Crew:* 250

Benson

US destroyer class. Experience with the single-funnelled *Gridley, Benham* and *Sims* Classes led to the design of a new type of general-purpose destroyer with two funnels. This was the result of adopting the 'unit' system of separating the boilers and turbines into two units, to reduce the risk of a single torpedo- or shell-hit putting all the machinery out of action. The adoption of longitudinal framing also gave greater hull strength.

The *Benson*s were basically similar to the *Livermore* Class, but incorporated minor differences because they were designed by Bethlehem. All except *Gleaves* and *Niblack* had the typical Bethlehem flat-sided funnels (cf British Thornycroft destroyers, which also adopted this Bethlehem 'trade mark').

Although the design specified quintuple banks of torpedo tubes, all except the *Hilary P Jones* and *Charles F Hughes* had quadruple tubes mounted temporarily. For the first time these were mounted on the centreline, a much better arrangement than the cumbersome broadside arrangement used in earlier classes. The guns on the after deckhouse were initially without shields, but were later given open-backed or closed shields.

The original antiaircraft armament was weak, as it was considered that five dual-purpose guns were sufficient. The 5-in gun at the forward end of the after deckhouse was replaced by two twin 40-mm gun-mountings late in the war, but the initial changes were restricted to increasing the .5-in machine-guns from four to 10 or 12, in single, twin and even quadruple mountings. The after bank of torpedo tubes was also removed, and by the end of the war the AA armament had been increased to two quadruple 40-mm mountings sponsoned aft, in addition to the two twins, which were shifted further forward, or seven single 20-mm.

Only one of the class was lost in the Second World War, the *Lansdale*, which was torpedoed off Cape Bengut, Algeria, while escorting convoy UGS-37 from Norfolk to Bizerta. In 1954 *Benson* and *Hilary P Jones* were transferred to Nationalist China (Taiwan) and renamed *Han Yang* (DD.15) and *Lo Yang* (DD.14). Both ships were stricken in 1975 but their names and numbers were given to later ex-US destroyers. The *Niblack, Charles F Hughes* and *Madison* were stricken for scrapping in 1968, but the *Niblack* was retained for floating dock trials at Davisville, Rhode Island, and the *Madison*

The seaplane carrier *Ben-My-Chree*—'Woman of My Heart' in Manx—under way off Mudros, on the Aegean island of Lemnos, in late 1916

Hull no and name	laid down	launched	completed	builder
DD.421 *Benson*	5/1938	11/1939	7/1940	Bethlehem, Quincy
DD.422 *Mayo*	5/1938	3/1940	9/1940	Bethlehem, Quincy
DD.423 *Gleaves*	5/1938	12/1939	5/1940	Bath Iron Works
DD.424 *Niblack*	8/1938	5/1940	8/1940	Bath Iron Works
DD.425 *Madison*	12/1938	10/1939	12/1940	Boston navy yard
DD.426 *Lansdale*	12/1938	10/1939	12/1940	Boston navy yard
DD.427 *Hilary P Jones*	11/1938	12/1939	12/1940	Charleston navy yard
DD.428 *Charles F Hughes*	1/1939	5/1940	12/1940	Bremerton navy yard

was sunk as a target. The *Gleaves* was stricken in November 1969 but was earmarked for preservation as a memorial, while the *Mayo* was stricken in 1970. A projected conversion of the surviving vessels to 'corvettes' (DDC), involving the removal of half the boilers and the improvement of the antisubmarine outfit, was dropped.

See also *Livermore* Class, *Bristol* Class.

Displacement: 1620 tons (standard), 2515 tons (full load) *Length:* 106 m (348 ft 0 in) oa; (DD.423, 428) 106.13 m (348 ft 3 in) oa; (DD.421, 422) 105.13 m (347 ft 3 in) oa; (DD.424) 105.91 m (347 ft 6 in) oa *Beam:* 10.91 m (36 ft 0 in) *Draught:* 5.42 m (17 ft 9 in) max *Machinery:* 2-shaft Westinghouse single-reduction geared turbines, 50 000 shp=37½ knots (max), 33 knots (full load) *Armament:* (As completed) 5 5-in (127-mm)/38-cal DP (5×1), later reduced to 4; 6 0.5-in (13-mm) AA machine-guns (6×1), (DD.421, 422

had 10, DD.423, 426, 428 had 4); 10 21-in (53-cm) torpedo tubes (2×5); (After 1945) 4 5-in/38-cal (4×1); 12 40-mm AA (2×2, 2×4) or 7 20-mm AA (7×1); 5 21-in (53-cm) torpedo tubes; 4 DCT *Crew:* 191 (peacetime), 276 (wartime)

Bentinck

British frigate class. The 46 vessels of this class were all constructed in the US by the Bethlehem Steel company and supplied to Britain under the lend-lease programme. They were similar to the *Bayntun* Class but were provided with a larger hull to accommodate a turbo-electric, instead of diesel-electric, machinery installation. This allowed for a return to the original designed power of 12 000 shp, providing a speed of 24 knots compared with 6000 shp and 21 knots in the *Bayntun* Class.

The designed armament was three 3-in

dual-purpose guns, four single 20-mm and one twin 40-mm, but several ships were completed without the latter, owing to a shortage of 40-mm mountings, and shipped two additional 20-mm instead. Later additions, both before and after completion, increased the 20-mm armament to ten or 12 singles. Early modifications carried out by the British included an increase in the depth-charge stowage to 200, while later several ships had a single 2-pdr pom-pom fitted as a bow-chaser for use against E-Boats. Wartime modifications resulted in a large number of variations in the light antiaircraft armament fitted: the data below gives the designed armament.

The class was commissioned during 1943-44 and served in the North Atlantic, English Channel and North Sea and with the Russian convoys. A large number were also employed as escorts for the Normandy invasion force. During 1944, 14 were converted into coastal forces control frigates for operations against enemy coastal shipping and E-Boats in conjunction with MTBs, MGBs etc. They operated exclusively in the English Channel and North Sea, being based either at Harwich or at Portsmouth.

They proved very successful in the antisubmarine role and ships of the class shared in the sinking of 25 U-Boats. The most successful were *Duckworth*, which sank two submarines and shared in the destruction of three more, and *Affleck*, which shared in the sinking of five. Two of the class were lost: the *Bickerton*, which was torpedoed by *U 354* in the Barents Sea on August 22, 1944, was so badly damaged that she had to be sunk by the destroyer *Vigilant*; and the *Bullen*, torpedoed by *U 775* northwest of Scotland on December

The *Bentinck* Class frigate *Riou* in 1945. Armament was modified as required: *Riou* here has three 3-in DP, and eight single 20-mm AA guns

Beretta

Beretta Model 1915 in 9-mm Glisenti calibre, a standard Italian army weapon

9-mm Model 1923 Beretta, a modified Model 1915/19 with external hammer

I V Hogg

The Beretta Model 949, or Tipo Olimpionico, a .22-in version of the Model 1915 with longer barrel and refined sights

I V Hogg

6, 1944. In addition no less than eight were damaged beyond reasonable repair—the *Duff*, *Dakins* and *Ekins* were damaged by mines, the *Affleck*, *Redmill* and *Whitaker* were torpedoed by submarines, the *Trollope* was torpedoed by an E-Boat and the *Halsted* was torpedoed by a German torpedo boat. However, the *Duff* was reprieved and subsequently repaired. Another, the *Affleck*, and an undamaged unit, the *Hotham*, were converted to floating power stations in 1945 for service in ports where electric power was short. The turbo/generator sets of these vessels made them ideal for this purpose.

All but one of the class, including those damaged, were officially returned to the US between 1945 and 1947. The only exception was *Hotham*, which remained in British service until 1956 when she was returned.

The class consisted of: *Affleck, Aylmer, Balfour, Bentinck, Bentley, Bickerton, Bligh, Braithwaite, Bullen, Byard, Byron, Calder, Conn, Cosby, Cotton, Cranston, Cubitt, Curzon, Dakins, Deane, Duckworth, Duff, Ekins, Essington, Fitzroy, Halsted, Hargood, Holmes, Hotham, Narbrough, Redmill, Retalick, Riou, Rowley, Rupert, Rutherford, Seymour, Stockham, Spragge, Stayner, Thornbrough, Torrington, Trollope, Tyler, Waldegrave, Whitaker.*

Displacement: 1347 tons *Length:* 93.27 m (306 ft) oa *Beam:* 11.22 m (36 ft 9 in) *Draught:* 2.80 m (9 ft 3 in) *Machinery:* 2-shaft turbo-electric drive, 12 000 shp=24 knots *Armament:* 3 3-in (76-mm) (3×1); 2 40-mm (1×2); 4 20-mm (4×1); 1 Hedgehog; 4 depth-charge throwers *Crew:* 186

Beretta

Italian pistols. The firm of Pietro Beretta entered the pistol field in 1915 with a 7.65-mm blowback automatic for the Italian army. The slide was cut away at the front to form arms which lay alongside the barrel, and an ejection port was cut in the top centre of the slide. No ejector was fitted, the spent cases being ejected by pressure of the firing pin. There was a prominent safety catch on the left side which also functioned as a stripping catch, and some models also carried a second safety catch at the rear of the frame. While 7.65-mm was the principal calibre, models were also produced for the 9-mm Glisenti cartridge and for the 9-mm Short cartridge.

After the war the design was improved in several details to produce the Model 1915/19. The cutaway section of the slide was made longer, so that it combined with the ejection opening, and the forward edges were swept up forming a bridge over the muzzle which carried the foresight. A new method of mounting the barrel was adopted and the safety catch was made smaller and more tidy. This model was produced only in 7.65-mm calibre, for police and military use.

The Model 1919 was then produced for commercial sale; this was a 6.35-mm version of the Model 1915/19 with the addition of a grip safety in the rear edge of the butt.

The Model 1923 was a 1915/19 modified to use an external hammer instead of an internal one. Chambered for the 9-mm Glisenti cartridge, it was only produced in small numbers, originally for military use and later for commercial sale.

The Model 1931 was much the same as the 1915/19 but with an external hammer. Most of these pistols were taken into use by the Italian navy and will frequently be found with wooden butt grips with a small medallion carrying the naval emblem, RM divided by an anchor. Commercial models, of which there were few, had black plastic grips.

The Model 1934 is the most common Beretta, and was the standard Italian army weapon from 1934 to 1945. It is little more than a Model 1931 chambered for the 9-mm Short cartridge. It was marketed commercially, but in small numbers since almost all production was taken by the army.

The Italian air force preferred the 7.65-mm calibre and they therefore adopted the Model 1935, which was simply the 1934 in a different calibre, sold commercially in some quantity.

In postwar years the Beretta company produced a wide range of pistols for commercial sale. The Model 318 was a refined 1919, sold in the USA as the Panther; the Model 418 was an improved 318, sold as the Puma; the Model 948 or Plinker was little more than the Model 1934 in .22 calibre, while the Model 949 or Tipo Olimpionico was a .22 Model 1915 with a longer barrel.

In 1951 the company produced a new military pistol, the M951 or Brigadier, the

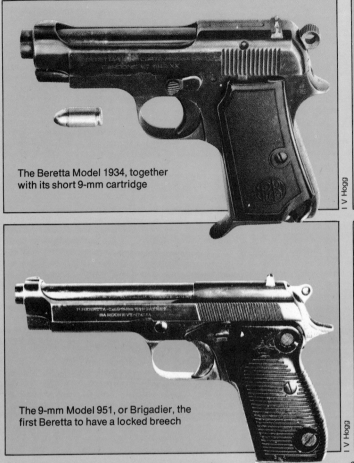

The Beretta Model 1934, together with its short 9-mm cartridge

I V Hogg

The .22-in Model 950 can be either breech-loaded or magazine-fed

I V Hogg

The 9-mm Model 951, or Brigadier, the first Beretta to have a locked breech

I V Hogg

Beretta Model 71 Jaguar, a .22-in Long Rifle round 'pocket pistol'

I V Hogg

first locked breech model to appear under the Beretta name. Using the usual Beretta configuration of open-topped slide and external hammer, it was locked by a wedge beneath the breech, similar in operation to that used with the Walther P-38 pistol. The safety catch was a cross-bolt in the frame. The original intention was to produce the pistol with a light alloy frame in order to keep the weight down, but this led to difficulties and the design eventually appeared with a steel frame. Chambered for the 9-mm Parabellum cartridge, it has been adopted as standard by the Italian, Egyptian and Israeli armies.

Beretta

Italian rifles. Although the Beretta company had been making sporting rifles for many years, their first venture into the military rifle field appears to have been the Fucile Automatico Beretta Modello 59 or BM-59. This was a rebuild of the US Garand M1 rifle to suit the 7.62-mm NATO cartridge.

For some years Beretta had been making the Garand under licence, both for use by the Italian army and for export—for example, to Indonesia—and the modifications to the Garand were based on their view of the requirements of a military rifle. The 8-shot clip-loaded magazine was discarded in favour of a removable 20-round box which can be charger-loaded whilst still in place on the rifle. The trigger and firing mechanism are improved and a combined grenade-launcher/flash-hider fits on the muzzle; this is removable in the parachutist version of the rifle, but permanently attached in the standard version. One of the most important changes was the incorporation of optional automatic fire.

A number of variants have evolved from this basic design. The standard rifle was adopted by the Italian army and has a light bipod fitted to the gas cylinder. The Mk 2 has a winter trigger and guard to allow firing in gloves, together with a pistol grip; the Mk 3 has two pistol grips and a folding stock of metal; the Mk 4 is a heavy-barrelled model for use as the squad automatic. In addition to their adoption by the Italians, these rifles have also been made under licence in Indonesia and Morocco.

After the success of the BM-59 series, the company looked at the assault rifle field and eventually produced the Model 70 in 5.56-mm calibre. This is a lightweight gas-operated rifle, constructed from steel pressings and stampings with plastic furniture. The flash-

COMPARATIVE DATA (Beretta pistols)

Gun	Mod 1915	Mod 1915/19	Mod 1934	M951
Weight (gm/oz)	610/21.5	975/34.4	750/26.4	820/28.9
Length (cm/in)	14.9/5.9	16.9/6.6	15.0/5.9	20.4/8.03
Barrel length (cm/in)	8.5/3.3	9.5/3.7	8.8/3.5	11.4/4.5
Magazine	7	8	7	8-10
Calibre	7.65-mm	7.65-mm	9-mm	9-mm
Muzzle velocity (m/sec/ft/sec)	250/825	250/825	265/875	396/1300

Beretta

hider/grenade-launcher is fitted, together with special flip-up sights for firing grenades, and a light bipod can also be fitted. Two versions have been produced, the assault rifle with fixed plastic butt and a special troops carbine with folding steel stock. Manufacture is to a high standard, but by the end of 1976 only the Malaysian army had adopted the weapon. (For comparative data see right.)

Beretta

Italian submachine-guns. Beretta entered the submachine-gun business in 1918, when the Italian army asked for a modification of the Villar Perosa machine-gun to make it a handier weapon.

The Villar Perosa was a twin-barrelled gun, firing pistol ammunition, but of inconvenient

Gun	BM-59 Mk 1	BM-59 Para	Model 70 Assault
Weight (kg/lb)	4.3/9.6	4.3/9.6	3.4/7.6
Length (cm/in)	109.5/43.0	111/43.7	95.5/37.6
Barrel length (cm/in)	49/19.3	46.7/18.4	45.2/17.8
Magazine	20	20	30
Rate of fire (rds/min)	800	810	700
Calibre	7.62-mm NATO	7.62-mm NATO	5.56-mm×45
Muzzle velocity (m/sec/ft/sec)	823/2700	800/2625	960/3150

The Beretta BM-59 automatic rifle, a rebuilt version of the American Garand M1 rifle to take the NATO 7.62-mm cartridge. A 20-round box replaces the Garand's 8-round magazine, a combined grenade-launcher/flash-hider is attached to the muzzle and a light tripod is fitted

form, and by taking the basic mechanism and barrel and allying it to a conventional wooden stock with folding bayonet, the Beretta Model 1918 was produced. The magazine fitted into the top of the weapon, and an ejection chute protruded from the bottom. This weapon remained in Italian army service throughout the Second World War. It was chambered and adjusted for the 9-mm Glisenti cartridge.

In subsequent years Tullio Marengoni, the Beretta designer, developed several sub-machine-gun designs but it was not until the late 1930s that one went into production. This was the Model 1938A, which had a short wooden stock, a slotted barrel jacket, a folding bayonet and a box magazine inserted through the bottom of the stock. The mechanism was of the conventional blow-back type, and the gun was of 9-mm calibre, chambered to take a special Italian army 9-mm cartridge which was of the same size as the 9-mm Parabellum but loaded to a slightly lower velocity. It was more powerful than the 9-mm Glisenti, and the guns could be used with standard 9-mm Parabellum cartridges.

Twin triggers were used, the forward one for single shots and the rear for automatic fire. The forward end of the barrel jacket was formed into a muzzle compensator which diverted some of the muzzle blast upwards

and thus kept the muzzle down, on target, while firing. Relatively few of the original type were made, and a modified design with round holes in the barrel jacket and a safety bar in the rear of the trigger guard was adopted for military service. There were also some minor changes made during the war in order to simplify production.

While the M1938A was probably one of the best submachine-guns of its day, it was difficult and expensive to make, and Maren-goni set to work to develop a simpler design. His first attempt was known, somewhat con-fusingly, as the Model 1 and was designed in 1941. This appears to have been influenced by the German MP38, and uses a folding metal stock and pistol grip, and does away with the barrel jacket. The twin triggers and the muzzle compensator were still used. Although a good design it was still too complicated, and it was not put into series production.

The next model, the 38/42, was produced by amalgamating the various features of the Model 1938A and the Model 1 and adding a few new ones. The M38/42 retained the short wooden stock of the 1938A with the un-jacketed barrel and compensator of the Model 1. A fixed firing pin was carried on the bolt face, and the receiver was of tubular

sheet steel. Issues of the 38/42 began in early 1943 and it was used by both Italian and German forces in Italy, as well as being sold to the Rumanian army in 1944.

In 1945 a slightly improved version of the 38/42, known as the 38/44, was produced, and this was adopted by Pakistan, Iraq, Costa Rica and Syria. A further modification of the basic design was the Model 38/49, which added a cross-bolt safety device in the centre of the stock. Numerous variants of this model were produced to satisfy prospective purchasers; some had perforated barrel jackets, some had folding bayonets, and some had folding stocks. They were sold throughout the world between 1949 and 1962.

A change of designation came with the next design, the Model 5. This was little more than a wooden-stocked 38/49 without the cross-bolt safety and with the addition of a grip safety just behind the magazine housing. This safety device must be squeezed in order to allow the bolt to move.

The Model 5, and certain minor variants, represented the last of Marengoni's designs. After his retirement his place was taken by Domenico Salza, who proceeded to embark on a development programme which resulted in the Model 12, which subsequently went into production in 1959.

COMPARATIVE DATA

Gun	M1918	M1938A	M38/42	Model 12
Weight (kg/lb)	3.3/7.2	4.2/9.25	3.3/7.2	3.0/6.6
Length (cm/in)	85.1/33.5	95.2/37.5	80.0/31.5	64.5/25.4
Barrel length (cm/in)	30.5/12.0	30.5/12.5	21.6/8.5	20.3/8.0
Magazine capacity	25	10, 20, 30 or 40	20 or 40	20, 30 or 40
Rate of fire (rds/min)	900	600	550	550
Calibre	9-mm Glisenti	9-mm Model 38A	9-mm Parabellum	9-mm Parabellum
Muzzle velocity (m/sec/ft/sec)	381/1250	419/1375	381/1250	381/1250

Beretta Model 1918/30, the Model 1918 revised to take a convention-ally-mounted magazine and 9-mm Parabellum, rather than Glisenti, cartridge

Early Model 6 Beretta, first stage in the development of the Model 12, with flared magazine feed for ease of loading and the twin triggers of the Model 1938/49

The late Model 6 was the first Beretta sub-machine-gun design to have the overhung, or telescoping, bolt inspired by the Czech CZ23

The Model 8 incorporated a stepped wooden grip around the perforated barrel jacket and a large extraction port, and was a cleaner and simpler version of the late Model 6

The Model 10 represented a complete change of design, and with the circular body, designed to make production easier, began to resemble the final Model 12

Left: The final Beretta Model 12 submachine-gun—the result of some six years' work by Domenico Salza and a complete change from earlier Beretta sub-machine-gun designs

Above: The early prototype Model 12 introduced the forward pistol grip, and the grip safety was moved from behind the rear grip to below the trigger guard to resemble the final design

I V Hogg

Bergmann

Beretta Model 1938/42, a simplified version of the 38A designed to simplify production using steel stampings, dispensing with the barrel jacket and fitting a new bolt

J S Weeks

The Model 12 is considerably different from its predecessors. It is largely made of stamped metal and plastic, designed so as to be put together easily and cheaply without sacrificing reliability There are two pistol grips, with the magazine between them, and much of the length of the barrel is concealed within the receiver. The bolt is of the 'over-hung' or 'telescoping' type, hollowed out to pass over the rear end of the barrel and thus bring the weight forward so as to improve the balance of the weapon, as well as to shorten it. The overhung portion of the bolt is slotted to allow cartridges to feed and eject. It was adopted by the Italian army in 1961 for use by special service troops and is also made under licence in Indonesia.

Bergmann

German machine-guns. Like every other weapon which came from the Theodor Bergmann Waffenbau AG of Suhl, these guns were designed by a Schmeisser, in this case Louis, father of the submachine-gun designer Hugo.

The first patents were taken out in 1901 and were for a water-cooled gun operated by recoil, a locking piece being cammed down from beneath the breech block, after which the block could continue to recoil and operate the feed mechanism. The barrel could be rapidly changed—an unusual feature in a water-cooled gun at this time—and feed was by a disintegrating-link belt.

The first model, the M 1902, met with little success, but after various improvements were incorporated it was at last perfected as the MG 10 of 1910. It was extensively tested by the German army, but it was never officially adopted, though numbers were sold throughout Europe.

During the First World War a much lightened version, called the MG 15nA (nA meaning *neuer Art*, or new type), was accepted for military service, being first issued in 1916. This used the same basic mechanism but with an air-cooled barrel. A pistol grip and shoulder stock were added, and feed was from a canvas belt carried in a side drum. This was a sound and useful weapon, weighing only 12.7 kg (28 lb) at a time when the light machine-

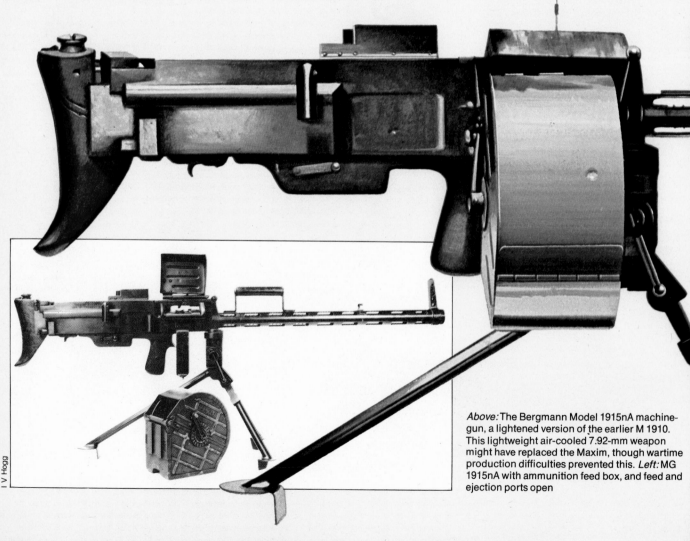

Above: The Bergmann Model 1915nA machine-gun, a lightened version of the earlier M 1910. This lightweight air-cooled 7.92-mm weapon might have replaced the Maxim, though wartime production difficulties prevented this. *Left:* MG 1915nA with ammunition feed box, and feed and ejection ports open

I V Hogg

John Walter Collection

Beretta Model 12 9-mm submachine-gun with stock folded and box magazine in position. The Model 12 has been issued to special units of the Italian armed forces, and is produced under licence in Indonesia

gun was hardly thought of, but it was adopted only in small numbers, the army apparently being suspicious of air-cooled guns for ground use.

(MG 15nA) *Weight:* 12.7 kg (28.5 lb) *Length:* 112.1 cm (44.13 in) *Barrel length:* 72.4 cm (28.5 in) *Rate of fire:* 500 rpm *Feed:* 250-round belt *Muzzle velocity:* 884 m/sec (2900 ft/sec) *Calibre:* 7.92-mm Mauser

Bergmann

German submachine-guns. The name Bergmann applies to several submachine-guns, but in fact only one was ever designed by a Bergmann.

The Bergmann company gave its name to the first real submachine-gun, but it was actually designed by Hugo Schmeisser, an employee of Bergmann, in 1916-17. The gun, designated the MP 18/1 (ie first modification of the MP 18), was introduced into German army service in the early summer of 1918 for use by storm-troops and NCOs. It was a blowback weapon firing from an open breech, using the 9-mm Parabellum cartridge and fed from the left side by using the 'snail' helical magazine which had already been developed for use with the long-barrelled Luger pistol. Some 35 000 MP 18/1 were manufactured before the war ended.

After the war submachine-guns were forbidden to the army but were permitted to be held by the German police forces, and numbers of the MP 18 were modified to become the MP 18/2, in which the magazine became a conventional straight box entering at right-angles to the axis of the gun, instead of the 45° of the snail magazine.

The MP 18/2 also had provision for firing single shots, and it was produced as a new

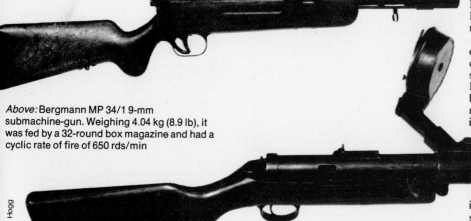

Above: Bergmann MP 34/1 9-mm submachine-gun. Weighing 4.04 kg (8.9 lb), it was fed by a 32-round box magazine and had a cyclic rate of fire of 650 rds/min

I V Hogg

Bergmann 9-mm MP 18/1, the first submachine-gun to be adopted by the German army, fitted with 'snail' helical magazine first developed for the long-barrelled Luger

gun by the C G Haenel company as well as being produced by modifying older weapons. It was later made under licence in Spain and Belgium and was commercially available in a number of different calibres.

Early in the 1930s Hugo Schmeisser produced a fresh design called the MK (Maschinen Karabin) 36. This used a wooden stock which resembled the standard Mauser Kar 98 carbine and could accept the carbine bayonet, but although the mechanism was much the same as his previous model, it incorporated a telescoping bolt cover which

infringed a patent owned by the Ermawerke, so the MK 36 never entered production.

Theodor Bergmann died in 1915, but in 1936 his son, Theodor Emil Bergmann, together with an engineer named Muler, designed a new submachine-gun. This fired from an open bolt, but had the non-reciprocating cocking handle at the rear of the receiver and had the box magazine mounted at the right-hand side of the receiver. The barrel casing was perforated, and there were two triggers; the forward

Bergmann-Bayard

trigger gave single shots, but when pulled harder it pressed the rear trigger to provide automatic fire.

The prototypes were made in Denmark, and the Danish army subsequently adopted the weapon; however, production in Germany was in the hands of the Carl Walther company, and it entered German army service as the MP34/1. It was also sold commercially, notably to Ethiopia, and turned up in some numbers in the Spanish Civil War. Some slight changes were made in the design, it was redesignated MP35/1, and was adopted by the Swedish army as their M/39. However, this contract was terminated by the outbreak of war.

In 1940 the Waffen SS adopted the MP35/1 as standard and had the manufacture transferred to the company of Junker & Ruh AG of Karlsruhe. The Waffen SS took the entire wartime production, some 40000 guns, and many specimens can be found with SS runes on the receiver.

Weight: (MP18) 4.62 kg (9 lb 4 oz); (MP28) 3.97 kg (8 lb 12 oz) *Length:* 812 mm (32 in) *Barrel length:* 196 mm (7.75 in) *Magazine capacity:* (MP18) 32-round drum; (MP28) 20/30-round box, 50-round 'snail' *Rate of fire:* 400 rds/min *Calibre:* 9-mm (0.354-in) *Muzzle velocity:* 381 m/sec (1250 ft/sec)

Bergmann-Bayard

German pistol. Theodor Bergmann designed a number of pistols in the 1890s, and was the first man to make a success of the blowback system of operation. But his ambition was to obtain a military contract, and for this he required a locked-breech design.

After various prototypes he took his machine-gun locking system, patented in 1901, and adapted it to a pistol design, offering the result commercially as the Mars pistol. To go with the new weapon he designed a new cartridge, the 9-mm Bergmann No 6, which used a longer cartridge case than the 9-mm Parabellum. The pistol used a vertically-moving locking piece to secure the breech and a six-round detachable box magazine in front of the trigger. In 1905 it was adopted by the Spanish army as their service pistol and Bergmann contracted manufacture out to the V Ch Schilling company of Suhl, since his own resources could not cope with both the commercial sales and the Spanish contract.

However, in his moment of triumph Bergmann was to be cast down; the Schilling company was taken over by Krieghoff, another gunmaker, who cancelled the contract to manufacture, so that Bergmann could not fulfil the Spanish order. He therefore withdrew from the pistol business, and licensed manufacture to the Ancient Etablissment Pieper of Liége, Belgium, who completed the Spanish order and also went on to produce the Mars under their own name.

Some small changes were then made, largely in order to accommodate the Pieper methods of working—the barrel was lengthened very slightly, the grip thickened, the rifling changed from four grooves to six and the barrel and barrel extension forged in one piece. The gun was then sold as the Bergmann-Bayard, Bayard being the trade name used by Pieper. The Greek army

Bergmann-Bayard 9-mm Model 1910 automatic pistol, manufactured by the Belgian firm of Pieper to a design by Theodor Bergmann

I V Hogg

adopted the pistol in about 1910, and the Danish army in 1911. Production by Pieper ceased in 1914 and was never resumed.

In 1922 the Danish army, requiring more pistols and being unable to obtain them from Belgium, began manufacturing their own. The design was slightly modified, the most visible alteration being the adoption of larger grips, and the pistol was known as the Model 1910/21. It remained in production until 1935 and in service with the Danish army until 1940. Both the Greeks and Spaniards ceased to use it shortly after the First World War, but the cartridge was still the Spanish service pistol cartridge in 1977, and is known as the 9-mm Largo.

Weight: 1.02 kg (2 lb 4 oz) *Length:* 254 mm (10 in) *Barrel length:* 101 mm (4 in) *Magazine capacity:* 6/10 *Calibre:* 9-mm (0.354-in) *Muzzle velocity:* 395 m/sec (1300 ft/sec)

Beriev Soviet aircraft See **Madge, Mail, Mallow, MBR-2**

Bermuda RAF name for US Brewster scout bomber See **Buccaneer**

Berserk

Swedish monitor class. These small monitors, or armoured gunboats, were built between 1871 and 1876, as smaller editions of the Ericsson monitors built in 1865-71.

With their low freeboard, one slow-firing gun forward and only 19 tons of coal, they were only capable of coast defence. The class underwent reconstruction in 1897-1909, when a 12-cm (4.7-in) quick-firing breechloader replaced the old 24-cm (9.45-in) Bofors Model '76 rifled breechloader, and the Gatling machine-guns were replaced by 57-mm quick-firers.

The machinery varied in power, the *Gerda* and *Hildur* developing only 133 ihp, but in other respects the ships were identical. They resembled the monitors of the American Civil War in appearance, with a flat deck, tall thin funnel and minimal superstructure.

All seven were in existence in 1914 but most were disposed of during the First World War; only *Björn* and *Gerda* were still nominally on the effective list by 1919. They disappeared shortly afterwards, among the very last of the traditional monitor-types.

Displacement: 452-460 tons (normal) *Length:* 40 m (131 ft 3 in) pp *Beam:* 7.9 m (26 ft 3 in) *Draught:* 2.5 m (8 ft 2 in) *Machinery:* 2-shaft reciprocating, 133-155 ihp=8 knots *Protection:* 76-95 mm (3-3¾ in) side, 420 mm (16½ in) gunshield *Armament:* (As built) 1 24-cm (9.4-in) RBL; 2 machine-guns; (As rearmed) 1 12-cm (4.7-in) QF; 2 57-mm (2.2-in) QF (2×1) *Crew:* 45

Name	launched	builder
Berserk	1874	Motala Verkstad, Norrköping
Björn	1874	Motala Verkstad, Norrköping
Folke	1875	Motala Verkstad, Norrköping
Gerda	1873	Bergsunds Mek Verkstad, Stockholm
Hildur	1872	Bergsunds Mek Verkstad, Stockholm
Sölve	1875	Motala Verkstad, Norrköping
Ulf	1873	Motala Verkstad, Norrköping

The Swedish monitor *Berserk* in about 1875. The 24-cm Bofors Model '76 rifled breechloader is concealed in a casemate below the forward canopy

Although the '88' was the backbone of German antiaircraft defence, the Luftwaffe (who were responsible for air defence) were sufficiently forward-looking to realize that it would not be long before its performance was outdistanced by newer and faster aircraft, and therefore the '88' should be reinforced by a more powerful weapon suitable for static emplacement.

10.5-cm Flak 38/39

At the end of 1933 a specification was put forward for a 105-mm (4.1-in) gun, demanding full power operation, a high rate of fire, good road mobility and a ceiling better than 10000 m (32808 ft). Krupp and Rheinmetall produced prototype models, one with electrical power operation and one with hydraulic from each firm. These were ready by early 1935 and went through a series of tests, after which each company produced four more guns for extended trials in the hands of troops during 1936. Finally, in October 1936, all the results were analysed and the Rheinmetall design using hydraulic power was selected as the production weapon, entering service as the 10.5-cm Flak 38.

In 1939, after more experience with the guns, some modifications were made. The electric motors on the mounting, which drove the hydraulic motors, were originally 220-volt DC, supplied with power from a mobile generator; these were now changed to 220-volt AC so that local domestic electric supplies could be used when available. Changes were made in the design of the gun barrel and in the system of data transmission from the predictor to the gun, and after these were all incorporated the gun was known as the 10.5-cm Flak 39.

The original wooden mock-up of Krupp's 10.5-cm Flak 38 heavy antiaircraft gun

I V Hogg

The Flak 38/39 was an effective weapon. It fired a 14.5-kg (32-lb) shell to 11400 m (37400 ft) at a rate of up to 15 rds/min, aided by an ingenious power rammer which propelled the cartridges into the breech by rubber rollers. Although originally proposed as a static weapon, it was sufficiently compact to be easily transported and eventually there were more in the mobile configuration than there were static. In addition some 116 were mounted on railway flat wagons so that they could be rapidly moved around to protect marshalling yards and other vulnerable targets on the railways. In all, about 2020 10.5-cm guns were in use with the German forces at the end of the war.

12.8-cm Flak 40

With the 105-mm design cleared for production in 1936, the Luftwaffe took another look at the current state of aircraft development and realized that even the 105-mm would soon be left behind. (In fact the 105-mm was outperformed by the 88-mm Flak 41 within six years.) The prime demand was always to get a higher ceiling from the gun, get the shell up to that ceiling as fast as possible, and have a good lethal area when the shell detonated, all of which argued a high-velocity gun. But since obtaining high velocity in small calibres was an expensive business, the easiest way to get results was to increase the calibre, and so

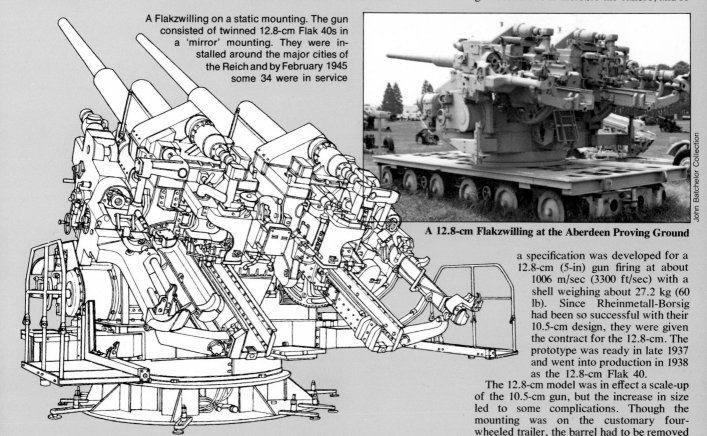

A Flakzwilling on a static mounting. The gun consisted of twinned 12.8-cm Flak 40s in a 'mirror' mounting. They were installed around the major cities of the Reich and by February 1945 some 34 were in service

A 12.8-cm Flakzwilling at the Aberdeen Proving Ground

John Batchelor Collection

a specification was developed for a 12.8-cm (5-in) gun firing at about 1006 m/sec (3300 ft/sec) with a shell weighing about 27.2 kg (60 lb). Since Rheinmetall-Borsig had been so successful with their 10.5-cm design, they were given the contract for the 12.8-cm. The prototype was ready in late 1937 and went into production in 1938 as the 12.8-cm Flak 40.

The 12.8-cm model was in effect a scale-up of the 10.5-cm gun, but the increase in size led to some complications. Though the mounting was on the customary four-wheeled trailer, the barrel had to be removed

Heavy Flak

for transport and carried on a separate trailer, an arrangement not well suited to an antiaircraft gun. After some experience with this system the Luftwaffe requested a one-load design, and a suitable trailer was produced by the Meiller company which allowed the whole gun and mounting to be lifted and carried in a single unit. However, the assembly was cumbersome—14.93 m (49 ft) long and weighing 26 417 kg (26 tons)—but before many were built a ban was placed on development of mobile guns over 10.5-cm calibre, and the remainder of the 12.8-cm production was of static-mounted guns, some of which were bolted down to railway flat wagons in a similar manner to the 10.5-cm gun. In all, six mobile, 362 static and 201 railway-mounted guns were built.

Right: A 12.8-cm Flak 40 on a rail mounting. By February 1945 there were six mobile guns and 362 fixed emplacements as well as 201 guns on railway mountings

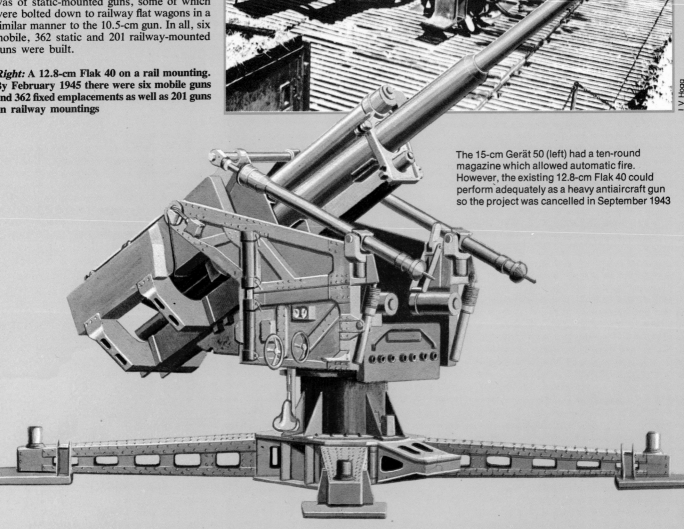

I V Hogg

The 15-cm Gerät 50 (left) had a ten-round magazine which allowed automatic fire. However, the existing 12.8-cm Flak 40 could perform adequately as a heavy antiaircraft gun so the project was cancelled in September 1943

15-cm Flak (Project)

In 1936, at the same time as they issued the 12.8-cm specification, the Luftwaffe also drew up a specification for a 15-cm Flak gun and gave this to Krupp to develop; shortly afterwards they also passed it to Rheinmetall-Borsig. Both companies produced prototypes in 1938, but when tested they proved to be a disappointment. The size of the weapons meant that they had to be transported in three loads—barrel, mounting and platform—which was slow and cumbersome. Moreover, their performance was no better than the 12.8-cm gun and there appeared to be no way of improving it. Some desultory work went into trying to improve the design, but after about a year the project was abandoned.

John Batchelor Collection

Loading the Krupp 15-cm Gerät 50 antiaircraft gun on to its mobile transporter

The barrel of the prototype 15-cm Flak on its trailer; the mounting is in the background

COMPARATIVE DATA

Gun	10.5-cm Flak 39	12.8-cm Flak 40	15-cm Flak project (estimated figures)
Weight in action (kg/tons)	10 224/10.06	13 000/12.8	—
Rate of fire (rds/min)	15	12	8
Elevation	85°	88°	85°
Muzzle velocity (m/sec/ft/sec)	881/2890	880/2885	1100/3600
Effective ceiling (m/ft)	9450/31 000	10 675/35 000	15 000/49 200
Shell weight (kg/lb)	14.8/32.63	26.02/57.3	51/112

But in spite of dropping that idea the Luftwaffe immediately produced a specification for an even more powerful 15-cm gun, demanding a 42-kg (92-lb) shell, a muzzle velocity of 960 m/sec (3150 ft/sec) and transportation in a single load—though it is difficult to imagine how they expected to get an answer when the best gunmakers had just spent four years on it.

By early 1942 Krupp had designed the gun —without the mounting—and fired it with some degree of success, but in October of that year all development of mobile AA guns was stopped in order to concentrate production on static weapons. Krupp and Rheinmetall were then asked to start again and design the guns as static guns, in the hope that improved performance could be obtained from them in this role (there being less of a weight restriction). However, just as they were beginning to make progress, all work on calibres over 12.8-cm was once again stopped so that production capacity could be devoted to aircraft and missile designs. In September 1943 the 15-cm Flak project was finally closed down.

24-cm Flak (Project)

A 15-cm (5.9-in) gun firing a 42-kg (92-lb) shell seems to represent the limit of this type, but in fact the Luftwaffe proposed two even heavier guns. In 1941 they drew up specifications for 21-cm (8.26-in) and 24-cm (9.45-in) guns. The 21-cm was to fire a 122-kg (270-lb) shell to 17 983 m (59 000 ft) while the 24-cm was to fire a 197-kg (435-lb) shell to the same height. At more or less the same time the German navy had drawn up specifications for 20.3-cm (8-in) and 24-cm antiaircraft guns for ship mounting in twin turret mounts. The armaments ministry now stepped in and persuaded the two arms to come to some agreement, and as a result in late 1942 it was decided to develop a combination of the Luftwaffe 24-cm gun in the navy's 24-cm twin turret. Contracts were issued, but the gunmakers appear not to have taken the idea very seriously and no design work was done other than some general arrangement drawings. Their excuse was that they would prefer to wait until the 15-cm project showed some results, since this would provide them with useful data, but once the 15-cm project was closed down the 24-cm project, predictably, went with it.

Heavy Antitank

At the outbreak of war the German army had no intention of going beyond 75-mm as their heavy antitank gun calibre, but events took charge and they soon had to change their plans. The 8.8-cm Flak gun had been used as an antitank weapon once or twice in Spain, as a result of which it became standard practice to provide piercing shell for every gun, but such employment was thought to be exceptional. However, in the desert Rommel showed that the '88' was extremely useful in dealing with armour before it got close enough to do any harm, which tied in well with the German tactic of drawing enemy armour into a screen of antitank guns before committing their tanks to battle, and it was decided, in 1940, to adapt all future designs of 8.8-cm gun to shooting in the ground role. This requirement was stated in a contract issued in 1940 for the new 8.8-cm antiaircraft gun, which became the Flak 41, and in the course of this development Krupp began working on a design of a 8.8-cm antitank gun, quite separate from the antiaircraft weapon of the same calibre.

8.8-cm PAK 43

The 8.8-cm PAK 43 was an outstanding weapon and one of the best antitank guns of all time. It broke new ground by using a four-wheeled carriage similar to antiaircraft gun practice, but dispensing with the usual high-set pedestal since ground guns demanded less elevation. As a result it had a low silhouette and was easily concealed in the field. The four-legged platform could be dropped from the wheels in under two minutes or, if time was short, the gun could be fired from its wheels. The gun was fitted with a semi-automatic vertical sliding breech, with electric firing.

The PAK 43 arrived on the Russian Front just in time: the Soviet T-34 and KV tanks were stretching the 75-mm guns to their limit,

The 8.8-cm PAK 43/41 showing the low silhouette. Though this was a very powerful antitank gun it was difficult to manhandle in action

Heavy Antitank

and the heavier punch and longer reach of the '88' was desperately needed. But the production of the new carriage was slow, and as a stop-gap measure the barrel of the PAK 43 was adapted to an emergency carriage thrown together from components which were in production for other weapons. The carriage trail legs came from the 10.5-cm le FH 18 howitzer, the wheels from a 15-cm howitzer, and a steel-plate saddle was specially made to marry these components together. The breech was modified by the adoption of a horizontal sliding block unit with electric firing. The result was a cumbersome weapon—it was rapidly nicknamed 'Barndoor' by the unfortunates who had to push it through the Russian mud—but it retained the full power of the PAK 43 and was well spoken of by its users. One report speaks of six T-34 tanks being knocked out in succession at a range of 3500 m (3828 yards), while another stated that a T-34 attacked from the rear to 660 m (656 yards) range had the engine block flung 5 m (5.5 yards) away from the tank.

12.8-cm PAK 44

For all the '88's success, there was the constant fear that at any moment the Allies might produce a more heavily-armoured or better-armed tank. Consequently, when the army asked for development of a 12.8-cm field gun in 1943, the gun designers decided to develop an antitank gun in this calibre as well. The result was one of the outstanding gun designs of the war, and it was fortunate for the Allied armour that the development came so late that none was produced in time to go into service before the war ended.

The gun was 55 calibres long and was mounted on a cruciform carriage similar to that of the 8.8-cm PAK 43. The Krupp prototype used two two-wheel axles at each end for transport, both being removed for firing. The Rheinmetall prototype used a four-wheel bogie on the front and a detachable two-wheel limber at the rear, the limber being removed for firing while the bogie swung up from the ground but remained on

Above: An 8.8-cm PAK 43 showing the well-sloped armoured shield. The gun could be fired from its wheeled carriage but it was more common practice to dig it in on its cruciform platform

The massive breech of the 8.8-cm PAK 43/41 L/71. Also visible is the spaced armour of the shield

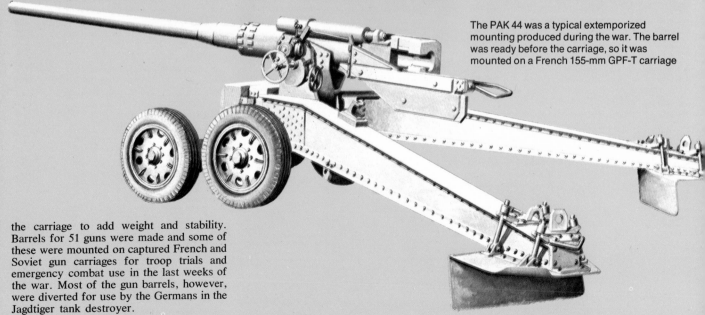

The PAK 44 was a typical extemporized mounting produced during the war. The barrel was ready before the carriage, so it was mounted on a French 155-mm GPF-T carriage

the carriage to add weight and stability. Barrels for 51 guns were made and some of these were mounted on captured French and Soviet gun carriages for troop trials and emergency combat use in the last weeks of the war. Most of the gun barrels, however, were diverted for use by the Germans in the Jagdtiger tank destroyer.

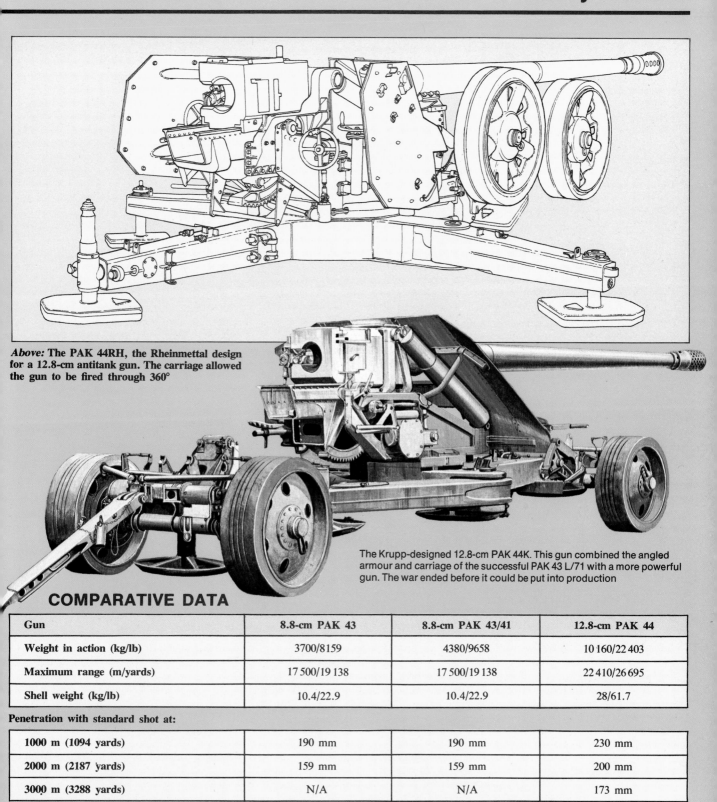

Above: The PAK 44RH, the Rheinmettal design for a 12.8-cm antitank gun. The carriage allowed the gun to be fired through 360°

The Krupp-designed 12.8-cm PAK 44K. This gun combined the angled armour and carriage of the successful PAK 43 L/71 with a more powerful gun. The war ended before it could be put into production

COMPARATIVE DATA

Gun	8.8-cm PAK 43	8.8-cm PAK 43/41	12.8-cm PAK 44
Weight in action (kg/lb)	3700/8159	4380/9658	10 160/22 403
Maximum range (m/yards)	17 500/19 138	17 500/19 138	22 410/26 695
Shell weight (kg/lb)	10.4/22.9	10.4/22.9	28/61.7
Penetration with standard shot at:			
1000 m (1094 yards)	190 mm	190 mm	230 mm
2000 m (2187 yards)	159 mm	159 mm	200 mm
3000 m (3288 yards)	N/A	N/A	173 mm
Penetration with tungsten shot at:			
1000 m	241 mm	241 mm	N/A
2000 m	184 mm	184 mm	N/A
Muzzle velocity with:			
Standard shot (m/sec/ft/sec)	1000/3281	1000/3281	1000/3281
Tungsten shot (m/sec/ft/sec)	1130/3700	1130/3700	N/A

Medium Field

This class of artillery in German service has always been filled by a variety of 10.5-cm, 13.5-cm and 15-cm weapons. The 10.5-cm have always been guns, long-barrelled and long-range supporters for the 10.5-cm howitzers, while the 15-cm class have been both guns and howitzers. The 13.5-cm calibre was a brief experiment before the First World War to try to reach a useful combination of shell weight and range, but neither of the two designs was ever perpetuated. In a similar manner, the closing period of the Second World War saw some development work on a 12.8-cm gun which was not brought to a conclusion.

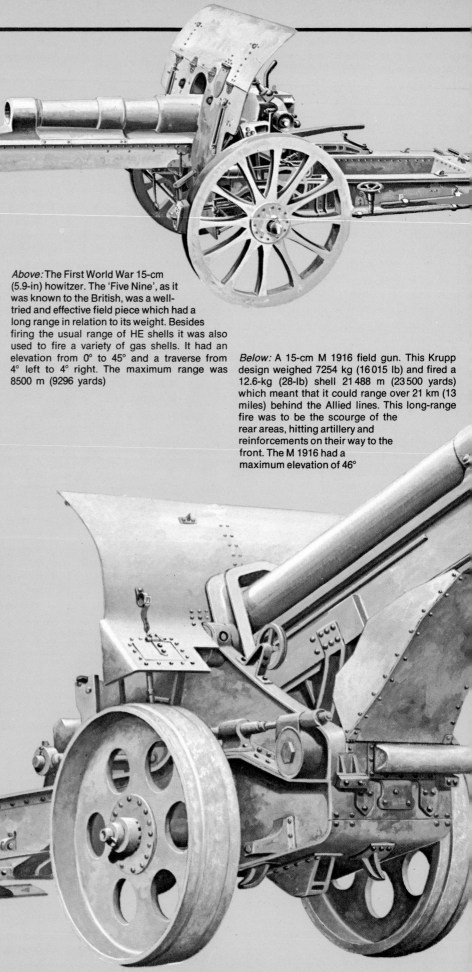

First World War Guns

The first modern equipment in the class was the 10.5-cm Feld Kanone (FK) 14, introduced in 1915. This was a box-trailed carriage with shield carrying a 35-calibre gun with sliding block breech, all made by Krupp. It formed a major proportion of the divisional heavy support during the First World War, though after 1917 it was supplemented by an improved version, the Model 17, which had a 45-calibre barrel and correspondingly better performance. These were backed up by the 15-cm Kanone 16, simply an enlarged model of the 10.5-cm weapon, and a 15-cm howitzer Model 13. This was the usual shorter-barrelled weapon firing a heavier shell and with the ability to lob the shell high in the air to drop behind cover.

schwere 10-cm Kanone 18

After 1918 several First World War guns remained in stock, but in the 1930s they were entirely replaced by a new generation of weapons. Among the first to appear was a new 10.5-cm gun, the schwere 10-cm Kanone 18. The order for this went to both Krupp and Rheinmetall in 1926, and after testing of their prototypes a combination of the Krupp carriage and the Rheinmetall gun was put into production. The carriage was a split-trail model with solid-tired wheels and the gun had to be hauled back in its cradle for towing by motor truck. For horse draught the barrel had to be removed completely and carried on a separate wagon in order to bring the load weight within the capabilities of the team.

It entered service in 1934, but was too heavy for horse teams and was gradually relegated to a coast-defence role where it was supplied with a special sea marker shell for ranging purposes.

Above: The First World War 15-cm (5.9-in) howitzer. The 'Five Nine', as it was known to the British, was a well-tried and effective field piece which had a long range in relation to its weight. Besides firing the usual range of HE shells it was also used to fire a variety of gas shells. It had an elevation from 0° to 45° and a traverse from 4° left to 4° right. The maximum range was 8500 m (9296 yards)

Below: A 15-cm M 1916 field gun. This Krupp design weighed 7254 kg (16 015 lb) and fired a 12.6-kg (28-lb) shell 21 488 m (23 500 yards) which meant that it could range over 21 km (13 miles) behind the Allied lines. This long-range fire was to be the scourge of the rear areas, hitting artillery and reinforcements on their way to the front. The M 1916 had a maximum elevation of 46°

I V Hogg

Above: A 15-cm sFH 18 captured in North Africa. Also visible is an 8.8-cm Flak.
Below: Soldiers of the British 8th Army inspect a 10.5-cm captured in Tunisia in 1942

I V Hogg

Right: A 15-cm M 1913 howitzer. In view of its barrel it was known as the 'Long Howitzer'. A highly effective weapon, it had a maximum range of 8500 m (9296 yards) and at normal rate could fire two rounds a minute

Medium Field

schwere 10-cm Kanone 18/40

The army were not happy with the sK 18 considering it too much gun for too little shell, and in 1937 they asked for a fresh design. Work went on at a low priority and the prototypes appeared in 1941, just after the invasion of Russia. This was not the best time to start thinking about a change in production and the idea was not pursued. As an experimental measure a number of new barrels were made and fitted to the old carriages to produce the schwere 10-cm Kanone 18/40. The new barrel was eight calibres longer, but the result was a weapon which weighed slightly more but managed to throw the same shell for approximately another 1828 m (2000 yards). This was hardly enough to warrant making a change, so the army refused to continue with the development and began to turn away from 10.5-cm in this class of weapon. After seeing what the Russians could do with their 122-mm guns, they asked for a fresh design in 12.8-cm calibre, but although development work went on until the end of the war no field equipments were ever made.

15-cm sFH 18

The medium howitzers were all of 15-cm calibre; numbers of the old Model 1913 had survived and were still in use throughout the war as reserve weapons, but the principal weapon was the 15-cm schwere Feld Haubitze 18. This was designed as a partner to the 10-cm sK 18, and used the same carriage, a normal method of rationalizing production, and except for the barrel dimensions there was little difference between them. It seems that the sFH 18 was expected to work at the limits of its performance: eight charges were provided, but the two highest charges were so erosive that they could only be fired under special authorization.

A German soldier with a 15-cm K39, ordered from Krupp by Turkey but taken by Germany

Above left: The breech and sights of a 15-cm sFH 18. *Right:* A German gunner removes the cartridge from the breech of a 15-cm sFH 18. *Below:* Gunners wrestle with a 15-cm sFH 18

15-cm sFH 36

In 1935 the army requested a redesign of the sFH 18, capable of being drawn in one load by horse team. Rheinmetall achieved this by rebuilding the carriage to incorporate a large amount of light alloy, and shortening the barrel. A muzzle brake was then fitted in order to cut down the recoil stresses on the lightweight equipment. A quick-release system allowed the gun to be disconnected from the recoil system and drawn back in its cradle for travelling, to spread the load more evenly, and an interlock ensured that the breech could not be opened unless gun and recoil system were properly connected again. This, the 15-cm sFH 36, was a first-class design, but production came to an end in 1942 as the war progressed and light alloy became a critical material.

Experimental Guns

The campaign in Russia led the army to demand new ideas for the field howitzer, leading to the remarkable Krupp and Skoda designs of le FH 43. Similarly, there was a demand for a new design of medium howitzer capable of all-round fire and a range of at least 18 km (11.2 miles). Krupp produced a design using a third trail leg under the barrel, very similar to that proposed by them for the 105-mm weapon, but they soon dropped this idea and combined the development programme with that which was in progress for the 12.8-cm PAK 44 antitank gun, by designing the mounting so that it would take either the antitank or the medium weapon. Another innovation was the use of bagged charges instead of cartridge cases, which were forced on the German designers by a growing shortage of brass. This had already been tried in an experimental weapon known as the 15-cm sFH 18/43, a normal sFH 18 with the sliding block breech rebuilt with sealing plates in the face of the breech block so that bag charges could be used. This development ended in 1945 but it was a useful starting point for the 120-mm gun used in the Chieftain.

The Skoda design of 15-cm sFH 43 never got past the drawing-board stage, though it appears to have been little more than a scale-up of their remarkable 10.5-cm le FH 43.

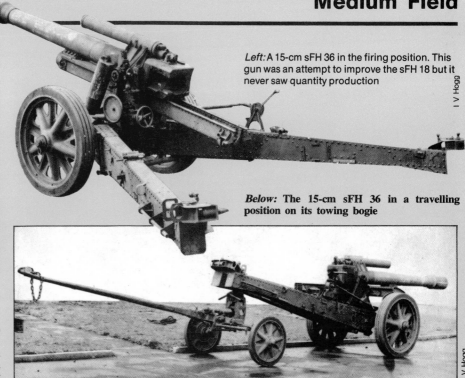

Left: A 15-cm sFH 36 in the firing position. This gun was an attempt to improve the sFH 18 but it never saw quantity production

Below: **The 15-cm sFH 36 in a travelling position on its towing bogie**

I V Hogg

COMPARATIVE DATA

Gun	Weight in action (kg/lb)	Maximum range (m/yards)	Shell weight (kg/lb)	Muzzle velocity (m/sec/ft/sec)
10.5-cm FK 14	2820/6217	13 100/14 325	18.75/41.33	585/1920
10.5-cm FK 17	3200/7054	16 500/18 045	18.75/41.33	650/2132
s 10-cm K 18	5642/12 438	19 075/20 860	15.14/33.37	835/2740
s 10-cm K 18/40	5680/12 522	20 850/22 800	15.14/33.37	880/2885
15-cm K 16	10 140/22 355	22 800/24 935	40.0/88.2	750/2460
15-cm H 13	2250/4960	8800/9623	44.0/97.0	375/1230
15-cm sFH 18	5512/12 154	13 250/14 490	43.5/95.9	495/1625
15-cm sFH 36	3280/7232	12 300/13 450	43.5/95.9	485/1590

A 12.8-cm K44 Krupp gun. This type doubled as a field gun and antitank weapon

I V Hogg

Rail Guns

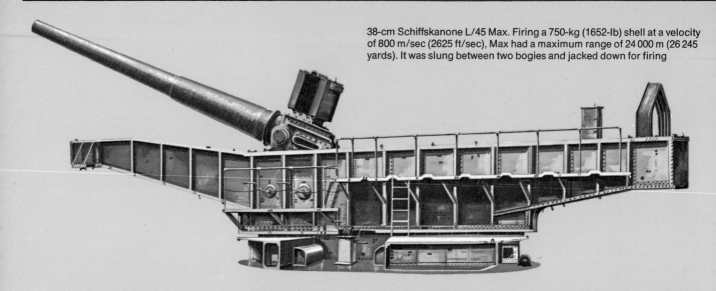

38-cm Schiffskanone L/45 Max. Firing a 750-kg (1652-lb) shell at a velocity of 800 m/sec (2625 ft/sec), Max had a maximum range of 24 000 m (26 245 yards). It was slung between two bogies and jacked down for firing

First World War Guns

Following the example of the French, the German army began developing railway artillery during the First World War. Most of these weapons were built around reserve battleships guns, for which suitable mountings were designed. One notable feature of German rail guns is that they were frequently given names, and since some of these names involved considerable development more details will be found under their name rather than in this short résumé. For further details see the entries under Anzio Annie, Bruno, Gustav, Kaiser Wilhelm Geschütz and Siegfried.

21-cm Peter Adalbert

The most common First World War designs were Peter Adalbert and Bruno. The former was a 21-cm naval piece mounted into a well-designed carriage consisting of a box girder supported on two six-wheel bogies. The gun was carried in a hydro-pneumatic recoil system within the box, and due to this construction, like most railway guns, could not be traversed more than a degree or so each side of its centreline. As a result it was necessary to build a curved track along which the gun could be pushed by a locomotive until the barrel was roughly aligned. After this the gun would be laid accurately by the traverse on the mounting.

Although the recoil system absorbed much of the recoil force, sufficient remained to push the whole gun back along the track for a few feet. Thus after a few shots had been fired it was necessary to bring up the locomotive and push the gun back until it again bore on the target area.

28-cm Bruno

Bruno was a 28-cm gun constructed around the barrels of the reserve stocks for the *Von Der Tann* Class battleships. This was mounted on an ingenious carriage, the Eisenbahn und Barbetten Gerüst—railway and barbette mounting—which, as the name implied, could be used as either a railway or a fixed gun. The usual sort of box-like body carried a small turntable beneath it, which could be bolted down to a prepared steel base dug deep into the ground. For normal railway use this was not required, but for semi-permanent emplacement a temporary track was laid across the prepared base, and the gun jacked up to enable the bogies to be removed, then lowered until the turntable could be bolted to the base. A number of these installations were used as coast-defence guns along the Belgian coast in 1917-18, the last two years of the First World War.

38-cm Max

The largest German rail gun of the First World War was the 38-cm (15-in) Max, the barrel of which came from the reserve stock of SMS *Bayern*. The mounting was again a simple box girder, but for firing it was usual to lower it onto a prepared turntable and remove the wheels, allowing a much greater arc of traverse.

This class of gun was also static-mounted as a coast-defence gun on the Belgian coast, but the railway versions were widely used on the Western Front, notably in the attack on Verdun.

21-cm 'Paris Gun'

Max was the basis for the greatest railway gun of the First World War, the famous 'Paris Gun' or Kaiser Wilhelm Geschütz, the long-range monster which shelled Paris from a range of 110 km (almost 70 miles). It was developed by Krupp and the German navy ordnance department, the theory being that if a shell could be propelled into the stratosphere extra-long range would come automatically due to the absence of air drag on the shell for most of its flight. The Max 38-cm gun was bored out and a 21-cm calibre liner inserted, so long that 12.89 m (42.3 ft) projected from the muzzle of the Max gun, and to the end of this was attached a 6-m (19.7-ft) smooth-bore extension. To prevent such length from collapsing under its own weight, extensive bracing was fitted over the barrel. The special shells were made with spiral ribs

One of the first German rail guns was an extemporization. The 17-cm gun Samuel was a standard heavy field piece anchored to a railway flat car. By pulling the trail to one side or other of the car the gun had 10° of movement either side of the centre line, while it also had the normal 12° of traverse on its carriage. The origin of the name Samuel is not known, but it was a common German practice to name rail guns

which engaged in the deep rifling, and since the propelling charge wore away the bore at an unheard-of rate, each shell was slightly larger than the one before and serially numbered so as to fit the bore throughout its expected life of 50 shells. Once the bore was worn beyond this point, it could be removed and returned to Essen, there to be rebored to 24-cm calibre.

Although on the standard Max rail mounting, it was emplaced by lowering it from the bogies on to a prepared concrete bed which carried an 8.53-m (28-ft) diameter roller race upon which the whole mounting could revolve. Three such emplacements were installed near Crépy-en-Laonnois, from which the guns opened fire on Paris on March 23, 1918. Other positions were also prepared near Fère-en-Tardenois and Noyon.

The first shells were fired on the morning of March 23, 1918, and in 44 periods of shelling a total of 367 rounds fell on various districts of Paris. The shelling stopped on August 9, however, as the Allied advances forced the gunners to retire. After the war no Allied Armistice Commission was able to find any trace of the guns.

Second World War Guns

When the Wehrmacht began to rearm, railway guns were high on the list of priorities. In order to simplify emplacement, the first requirement was to design a portable turntable which could be rapidly installed at the end of any convenient stretch of line and onto which any railway gun could be run. The gun mounting was then anchored to the turntable by a heavy hydraulic recoil system so that there was no danger of the mounting rolling off the turntable when the gun fired.

The German railway guns of the Second World War fall into two groups: those built as part of a long-term programme, largely very long-range super-guns, and those built in a crash programme begun in 1936 and intended to provide the army with a reasonable selection of guns by the summer of 1939.

15-cm K(E)

Of the long-term programme, the smallest gun was the 15-cm Kanone in Eisenbahnlafette (15-cm K[E]). This had the gun turntable mounted on top of a simple flat wagon, supported by outriggers which could be swung to the side of the track. Although an efficient design it was too small, there being little value in a railway gun of this calibre. Eighteen were built, after which the design was changed by placing a 17-cm gun on the same mounting. These guns were in fact old casemate guns from the *Deutschland* Class of pre-Dreadnoughts and dated from 1902, so this could hardly be called an improvement. The army agreed, and only six were built, in 1938.

21-cm K(E)

The major reason for the long-term programme was to develop super-artillery for extreme long-range bombardment, and this was typified by the 21-cm K(E) which was issued in March 1939. This was an enormous gun, with a 33.53-m (110-ft) barrel, in which the usual system of rifling was abandoned for a system using eight deep grooves, with shells having eight ribs to match. This system was adopted because there were doubts as to whether a conventional system of rifling and a copper driving band on the shell would withstand the enormous stresses developed in such a powerful weapon. The idea had been used in the Paris Gun in 1918, so there was ample information on which to base the design.

The mounting for the 21-cm gun was a simple box girder carried on two sets of bogies, the front set two ten-wheelers and the rear set two eight-wheelers. The barrel had to be braced to stop it drooping under its own weight and in order to allow it to recoil without striking the track beneath, it was necessary to jack up the entire mounting one metre above the bogies before firing.

Although the gun was technically a success the army were not pleased with the need to jack it up for every shot, and a second

A 28-cm Kanone 5(E) fires from its emplacement near Calais

Robert Hunt

Rail Guns

equipment was designed, using huge pneumatic balancing rams so that the barrel could be trunnioned further back and thus the recoil would not strike the ground. One of these was built, making two 21-cm guns in all, and both were used in 1940 to bombard Kent, one shell falling near Chatham, 88.5 km (55 miles) from the nearest point on the French coast across the Channel.

28-cm K5(E)

At the same time as the 21-cm K(E) began design, a 28-cm of more conventional form was put on the drawing board. This was the 28-cm K5(E) which was to become the standard railway gun and was one of the finest ever designed. This also used the deep-groove system of rifling, but was otherwise quite normal, no barrel bracing or jacking-up being required. It was carried on the usual sort of mounting, on two twelve-wheel bogies. The original version, issued in 1937, fired a conventional shell to 61.2 km (38 miles). Work then began on a rocket-assisted shell which extended the range to 86.9 km (54 miles). Then a barrel was smooth-bored to 31-cm calibre and a Peenemünde Arrow Shell developed which extended the range still further, to 151.3 km (94 miles). The K5(E) was used to shell Allied troops on the Anzio beachhead, and thus became known as 'Anzio Annie'. Eventually 28 of these guns were built.

28-cm Bruno

Most of the 'crash programme' guns were of the Bruno class. As might be guessed from the name, the first of the series was adapted from the First World War mounting drawings held in Krupp's archives, suitably altered to take a 24-cm barrel of naval origin. This became Theodor Bruno; a similar 24-cm barrel, slightly longer, became Theodor.

Theodor and Theodor Bruno were mounted on almost identical mountings, adapted from a First World War design, and attached by a rectangular cradle, made up from steel castings, which contained the recoil system. A small amount of traverse could be obtained by turning a hand screw.

The 28-cm Kanone 5(E) 'Leopold' or 'Anzio Annie' at the Aberdeen Proving Ground

The remainder of the Bruno guns were of 28-cm calibre; the first was kurz Bruno, so called because it used a 40-calibre (ie 40×28 cm long) naval barrel. Lang Bruno, on the other hand, used a 45-calibre 28-cm barrel. The third weapon of this calibre to use an old barrel was the schwere Bruno which used a heavier barrel (hence the name) of which two were found in stock. Finally came Bruno neue, the name being due to the barrel being newly designed; this was developed in 1938-9 because the army were dissatisfied with the performance from the old barrels, but only three were built. More were intended but the better performance of the 28-cm K(5) together with an unexplained ballistic irregularity in the Bruno neue which led to inaccurate shooting and dangerously high bore pressures resulted in the contract being cancelled so that work could be concentrated on the 28-cm K(5).

20-cm K(E)

In 1938 Krupp (the firm which made all German railway guns) were building 20.3-cm guns for the *Blücher* Class heavy cruisers. Eight guns were surplus to requirements and

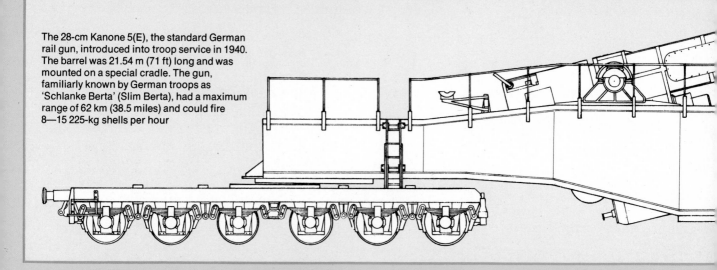
The 28-cm Kanone 5(E), the standard German rail gun, introduced into troop service in 1940. The barrel was 21.54 m (71 ft) long and was mounted on a special cradle. The gun, familiarly known by German troops as 'Schlanke Berta' (Slim Berta), had a maximum range of 62 km (38.5 miles) and could fire 8—15 225-kg shells per hour

Above left: A 28-cm schwere Bruno K(E) in action in 1940 against French positions. The gun fired a 284-kg (625.8-lb) shell up to 36 100 m (39 500 yards). *Right:* The 21-cm Kanone 12 with the upper carriage raised on its jacks into the firing position. Two such guns were built in the late 1930s

the army took them, asking Krupp to make suitable mountings. Krupp complied by simply taking out the First World War drawings of the Peter Adalbert gun, making a few alterations and putting the design into production again.

Soon after work had begun the army realized that they were about to be given eight guns of a calibre which was not standard to the army. They therefore asked Krupp if the guns could be bored out and rerifled to 21-cm, a standard army calibre. But it was too late, the guns were completed and the barrels already rifled, and the army had to take them as they were.

After their delivery in 1940, plans were made for making eight new barrels in 21-cm calibre, ready for the time when the original barrels wore out. Four of the new barrels had been built and the other four were under construction in 1944. But six of the guns were captured by the Allies in late 1944, so the programme was dropped.

28-cm K(5)

Towards the end of the war, with air attacks increasing, movement of railway guns became difficult. In 1943 a programme was begun for developing a new type of weapon, a railway gun which could be carried by road

if necessary, in order to bypass bomb-damaged tracks. The 28-cm K(5) was to be modified to have a platform beneath the centre of the mounting. If held up by damaged track, the gun could be lowered onto this platform and the bogies removed. Two special tractors, built from modified Tiger

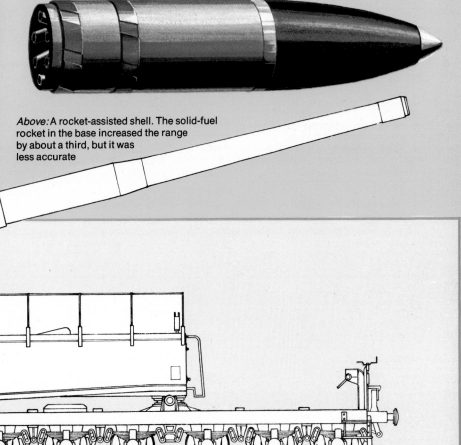

Above: A rocket-assisted shell. The solid-fuel rocket in the base increased the range by about a third, but it was less accurate

Rail Guns

The 31-cm Peenemünde Arrow Shell, designed for a smooth-bore version of the 28-cm K(5) rail gun. The shell had a range of 149.6 km (93 miles)

The 80-cm giant Gustav emerges from a railway cutting during the siege of Sebastopol in 1942

tank chassis, would then carry the barrel, another the breech mechanism, and two more would move under the ends of the mounting and carry it (thus the whole weapon could be driven around any obstacle) or, if required, could take the gun to any position and place it in action on the platform. The project was still in the planning stage when the war ended, but many of its basic features were to be seen in the American 28-cm M65 gun which appeared some years later.

80-cm K(E) Gustav

The largest German rail gun, in fact the largest (though not the largest calibre) gun ever made, was the monster 80-cm K(E) Gustav. Briefly, the facts are as follows. The complete weapon weighed 1350 tons and was transported piecemeal on a number of railway trucks, part of the mounting travelling on its own wheels. Upon reaching its firing position special track had to be laid to accommodate the mounting and its assembly crane, after which the task of putting Gustav together took three or four weeks. When assembled the gun was 43 m (141 ft) long, 7 m (23 ft) wide and 11.6 m (38.06 ft) high.

Gustav was built between 1937 and 1942 and was used in action at Sebastopol; it was then sent to Leningrad but the siege was raised before it could be emplaced. It is reported to have been used near Warsaw in 1944, after which it vanished. Parts of it were found by troops of the US 3rd Army, but the complete gun was never recovered. The only traces discovered were spare ammunition and a barrel found in Germany.

COMPARATIVE DATA

Gun	Weight in action (kg/ton)	Length overall (m/ft)	Maximum range (m/yd)	Shell weight (kg/lb)	Muzzle velocity (m/sec/ft/sec)
17-cm K Samuel	60 000/59.05	—	24 000/26 250	62.8/138.5	815/2675
21-cm K Peter Adalbert	—	—	25 580/27 975	115/253.5	780/2560
38-cm K Max	274 330/270	—	47 500/51 950	400/882	800/2625
15-cm K(E)	74 000/72.8	20.10/65.9	22 500/24 600	43.0/94.8	805/2641
17-cm K(E)	80 000/78.73	20.10/65.9	27 200/29 750	62.8/138.5	875/2870
20.3-cm K(E)	86 100/85.75	19.45/63.79	37 000/40 465	122/269	925/3035
21-cm K12(E)	302 000/297.23	41.30/139.49	115 000/125 765	107.5/237	1500/4922
28-cm K5(E) (1)	218 000/214.55	41.23/135.28	62 180/68 000	255.5/563.4	1128/3700
(2)	—	—	86 500/94 587	248.0/546.8	1130/3710
(3)	—	—	151 000/165 135	136.0/300	1524/5000
28-cm Bruno (WW1)	123 00/121	22.8/75	25 580/27 950	115/253	780/2560
24-cm Theodor	95 000/93.5	18.45/60.5	26 750/29 250	148.5/327.4	810/2658
28-cm kurz Bruno	129 000/126.98	22.8/75	29 500/32 260	240/529.2	820/2690
28-cm schwere Bruno	118 000/116.15	22.8/75	35 700/39 040	284/626.2	860/2820
80-cm Gustav (with HE shell) 1	350 000/1328.9	42.97/141	47 000/51 400	4800/10 582	820/2690

Note: Figures for 28-cm K5(E) refer to (1) standard shell; (2) rocket-assisted shell; (3) Peenemünde Arrow Shell in smooth-bore 31-cm barrel

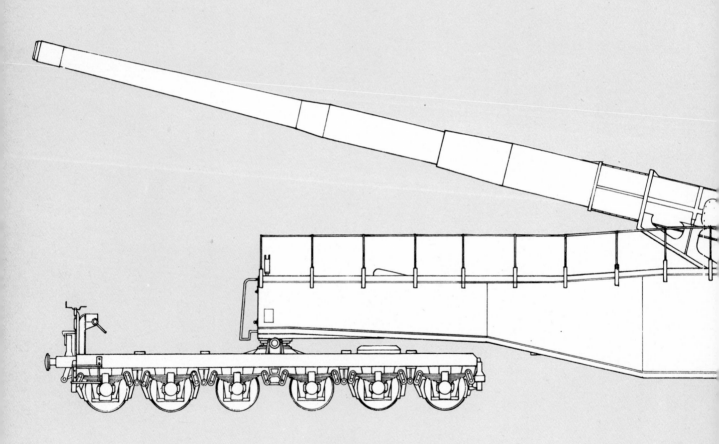